Rivers, Man and Myths

Rivers, Man and Myths

*From Fish Spears
to Water Mills*

Robert Brittain

DOUBLEDAY & COMPANY, INC., GARDEN CITY, NEW YORK
1958

For Mary

C'est son amour qui me rend ainsi fort
Pour conjurer les dangers du fleuve.

ACKNOWLEDGMENTS

One of the principal pleasures of studying a given subject and attempting to write about it is the rediscovery of human kindliness and generosity. It was a grant from the Foundation for World Government that first enabled me to begin the researches that led to this work, and I am very grateful to Dr. Stringfellow Barr and the other directors for this encouragement. To the scores of busy people who have allowed me to interrupt their work and have patiently heard and answered my questions, procured books, translated passages, secured illustrations, corrected my errors, and made valuable suggestions, I can only offer again, in print, my deepest thanks. To some my debt goes far beyond the usual mutual assistance which scholars offer to one another. I am deeply grateful to those who have read portions of my manuscript dealing with subjects in which they have special competence: Dr. B. Subbarao, Head of the Department of Archaeology at the University of Baroda, India; Miss M. S. Drower, Lecturer in Ancient History at University College, London; Dr. Joseph Needham of Gonville and Caius College, Cambridge; E. G. R. Taylor, Professor Emeritus of Geography, Birkbeck College; and Dr. Elsbeth Jaffe of the editorial staff of *A History of Technology*. To Mary Zwemer Brittain I am indebted not only for unfailing encouragement and constant assistance with multitudinous details of the work, but especially for her scholarly help in dealing with material concerning Arab civilization. F. LeGros Clark and Dr. Russell Ames have freely given their time and their editorial skill, as have the editorial staff of Doubleday & Company, Inc., New York, and of Longmans, Green & Co., Ltd., London, and I am most grateful for their valuable assistance. All these have helped to make my work better; none should be held responsible for whatever errors and shortcomings it may still exhibit.

The following publishers have permitted me to quote excerpts from books they have published:

Cambridge University Press: *Water Transport: Origins and Early Evolution,* by James Hornell; *Science and Civilisation in China,* by Joseph Needham.

E. P. Dutton & Co., Inc. and J. M. Dent & Sons, Ltd.: Ovid's *Metamorphoses* in the Arthur Golding translation, from the "Everyman's Library" edition.

Harvard University Press and William Heinemann, Ltd.: material from the following titles in the Loeb Classical Library: *Frontinus: The Aqueducts of Rome,* translated by Charles E. Bennett; *Vitruvius on Architecture,* edited and translated by Frank Granger; *Anthologia Graecae,* translated by W. R. Paton; and *The Geography of Strabo,* translated by H. L. Jones.

Oxford University Press: *Twin Rivers,* by Seton Lloyd; *The Story of Water Supply,* by F. W. Robins.

Penguin Books, Ltd.: *The Histories,* by Herodotus, translated by Aubrey de Selincourt; *The Persian Expedition,* by Xenophon, translated by Rex Warner; *Iran,* by R. Ghirshman; *Rome beyond the Imperial Frontiers,* by Sir Mortimer Wheeler; and *The Art and Architecture of the Ancient Orient,* by Henri Frankfort.

Orient Longmans: *New India's Rivers,* by Henry C. Hart.

Two publishers have extended the signal courtesy of allowing me to study copyright material before its actual publication: I am indebted to the Clarendon Press, Oxford, and to the editors of *A History of Technology* for permitting me to use the manuscript of Professor R. J. Forbes's chapters in the second volume of that work, which has since been published; and to the Cambridge University Press and to Dr. Joseph Needham I owe much significant material derived from galley proofs and manuscripts of the later volumes of their monumental *Science and Civilisation in China,* of which only Volumes I and II have been published to date.

CONTENTS

Acknowledgments 7

I. The Making of Man's World 17

II. The Savage by the Stream 32

III. Ditches and Dams 53

IV. Kings, Traders, and Soldiers 80

V. The River in the Mind 115

VI. Streams of Persian Gold 141

VII. The Wide Arch of Empire 175

VIII. The Rivers Beyond 200

IX. Rivers Enslaved 219

X. Wheels at the Cistern 235

XI. The Glory That Was 260

Some Suggestions for Further
Reading 274

Index 277

ILLUSTRATIONS

Maps

1. Areas in which ancient Mediterranean civilizations flourished   12
2. Ancient civilized lands of the Far East   13

Plates following page 120

1. The earliest known representation of a river (paleolithic engraving)
2. The river as center of the universe (Babylonian clay tablet)
3. The river becomes a source of food (floor engraving in Niaux cavern)
4. The river as the nourisher of crops (*shadufs*, the earliest water-lifting machines, and man-made canals —Assyrian bas-relief)
5. The role of the king in early riverine societies (detail from a protodynastic Egyptian macehead)
6. The river in ancient warfare (bas-relief from Nineveh)
7. Sennacherib's artificially irrigated gardens (bas-relief from Kuyunjik)
8. The descent of the Ganges (detail of statue of the dancing Siva)

9. The river as divinity (statue of "Great Mother" goddess wearing river as dress)
10. The river as place of recreation (Egyptian tomb painting of a hunting scene in the marshes)
11. The wide arch of empire (the Roman aqueduct near Tarragona, Spain)
12. Interior of the Byzantine cistern in Istanbul
13. The river as teacher of geography (Shalmaneser's discovery of the source of the Tigris)
14. Water wheels at Hama in Syria, an example of the earliest water-powered machines
15. The wheel at the cistern (Mogul painting of animal-powered water-lifting machine or *saqiyah*)
16. The idea of a multipurpose structure (barrage bridge over the Karun River at Shushtar, Iran)
17. A Moslem "earthly paradise" (mosaic from the Great Mosque in Damascus)
18. The food of the riverine cities (early Greek toy, representing a mule carrying an enormous fish)
19. Carnival on the river (Chinese Dragon Boat Festival, from an eighteenth-century tapestry)

Drawings

1. Evolution of water-lifting machinery   222
2. Evolution of grain-grinding machinery   223

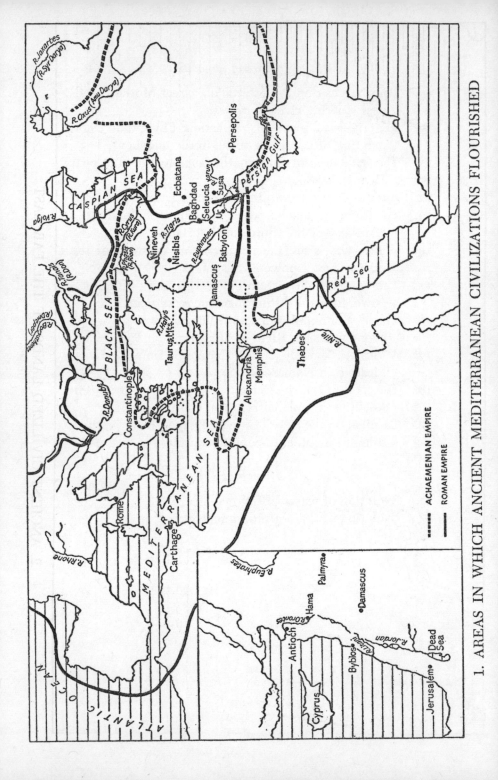

1. AREAS IN WHICH ANCIENT MEDITERRANEAN CIVILIZATIONS FLOURISHED

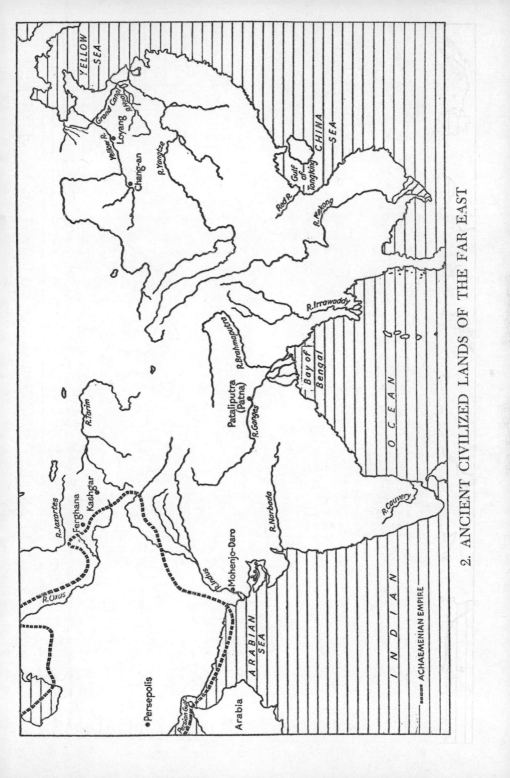

2. ANCIENT CIVILIZED LANDS OF THE FAR EAST

Rivers, Man and Myths

CHAPTER I

The Making of Man's World

BETWEEN men who change nature consciously and rivers whose work is witless, there is a deep affinity. It is a strange relationship, shifting and uncertain, established by men themselves in an infinite series of audacities and maintained at their own peril. They have never succeeded in taming the river as a dog is tamed, but neither have they ever been able to put it out of their minds. It has been teacher and slave, beast of burden, deified giver of life, demonic destroyer, scavenger—the relationship constantly changing as men themselves have changed. From the river men have drunk and lived, or they have drunk and died; from its sinuous body, ceaselessly moving yet remaining fixed, they have drawn their profoundest symbols of man's fate. Not yet fully used, never completely controlled, the river has been, of all natural forces, the one most intimately involved in human development at every stage.

If rivers had not been here in the first place, neither men nor any other form of life could have evolved. For countless ages before living things appeared, rivers, along with other natural forces, had been shaping and changing the surface of this planet. Before the first rains fell, the smooth crust that had once been molten rock had already cooled and hardened, and then had been broken up into a crazy-quilt of enormous fissures, depressions, and jutting peaks, as the still-boiling core attempted to break through the rind congealing around it. But fractured and crumpled as it was, the surface was still all rock, and it could be nothing else until inner heat and outer cold created an atmosphere, from which water condensed and began to fall.

From those first rains, which apparently fell without ceasing for millions of years, rivers were born. Some of the water fell directly into the deepest depressions, where it slowly accumulated to form the beginnings of oceans; but that which happened to land at any higher point began instantly to rush downward, by whatever route it could find, to the low-lying gulfs. Down the jagged peaks and sloping plains the water poured in a myriad small torrents. Whenever one of these reached a point where its headlong descent was slowed by a barrier or a less precipitous fall, it twisted aside into the bed of another torrent that had found a more direct downward path, and the two streams rushed on as one, to be joined at lower stages by many other tributaries, until they all swept in one wide flood into the depressions where all the waters were coming to rest.

This primordial passage of water over all the upthrust portions of the stony crust changed the surface of a bleak and moonlike planet into an earth. The rains attacked the rock with irresistible weapons. Since water is the most powerful natural solvent, it could soak into most of the rocks, loosening the chemical bonds that held them together and changing them into weaker compounds that would disintegrate more easily. In igneous rocks thrown up by earlier

18

volcanoes, the alkalis, when saturated with water, broke down into removable carbonates; the alumina and some of the silica went soft and became clay, through which were scattered particles of more resistant materials like quartz and white mica.

Besides such chemical changes there were enormous physical ones. By the sheer force of its downward rush, the water clawed and hammered and gouged at the crumbling rock, tearing off weakened particles, filing down the harder ones, until in time the mountains slowly shrank under the perpetual assault and on their less steep sides the rivers slackened the pace of their destruction. In the meantime, the water's chemical ability to hold other chemicals in solution and its physical ability to lift and carry particles of heavier matter had enabled it to take up the pulverized mountains and cart them away to the seas, flinging out bits and pieces all along the courses of the rivers to form the soils in which plants would eventually grow. Fragments too heavy to be carried were nevertheless pushed along, their rolling and scraping against other fragments adding a grinding tool to the river's arsenal.

At length the continual downpour slackened, as the planet cooled to the point at which no new water was created in the atmosphere. Rains still fell, but they were interrupted by short periods of respite, and gradually these intervals lengthened until stability was achieved. The sum total of water in earth and sea and air reached its final quantity, creating a situation, perhaps unique in the history of the universe, in which life could appear. And then occurred one of the miracles of creation: the water did not begin a long diminution, in which it would gradually seep outward into space. Instead, it began to move through a cycle of change, passing continually from one state to another without the slightest alteration in its total quantity.

From the seas it rose in invisible droplets, lifted by the heat from the sun. Cooling in the upper air, it condensed into clouds and was blown here and there by the winds in the lower levels of the atmosphere. Thence at length it returned to the earth as rain or snow or hail. Reaching the ground, some of the water soaked into the softened earth, to come to rest in that incalculable reservoir beneath our feet whose surface we call the water table, from which it might eventually be lifted through the roots and bodies of plants to be exhaled once more into the skies. The remainder immediately began to flow across the land, through rills and tiny rivulets, into brooks and streams, and finally into the wide channels through which it could reach the sea. It is that phase of the hydrologic cycle, in which the water passes from the time it strikes in separate drops upon the earth until it flows with a mighty current into the oceans where it comes to rest, that constitutes the rivers. It is in that phase that water has been of most intimate concern to human beings.

The ultimate over-all result of river flow is the gradual lowering of all the land that rises above the level of the oceans. At the present time, the average gradient is far less steep than it was when rivers began, yet rivers are still stripping off and dumping into the sea some eight thousand million tons of decayed rock every year. This colossal transportation results, however, in a general lowering of elevation by only one foot in every 9000 years. This is an average: a fast stream like the Irrawaddy cuts its basin down one foot in 400 years, while the sluggish rivers that amble across the plains of Siberia need 40,000 years to accomplish the same amount of denudation.

The principal cutting work of a river is done at its head. As long as a river exists, it grows constantly by cutting backward into the watershed that feeds it. This habit has produced a number of startling changes in the earth's structure and scenery. Many rivers have kept cutting away until they have made a chasm right through the watershed ridge and have even reached the bed of some other river flowing down the opposite slope. Some of these invaders have thereupon captured the water of the invaded stream and turned it into their own channels, leaving only a dry gravel bed to mark its former lower course. Sometimes the invaded stream has been merely "beheaded," and has continued to take down its lower valley the waters from a smaller drainage area. The Thames, for example, has been beheaded, possibly more than once, and is only the remnant of what was formerly a far longer river that drained a much greater basin.

The Jordan, the Litani, and the Orontes are apparently three sundered portions of what was once a single river, fed by run-off from the parallel mountain ranges of Lebanon and flowing southward in the valley between them all the way from Syria down into the Jordan Rift and on to the Dead Sea. But on the other side of the western range, two lively mountain streams rushing down into the Mediterranean began cutting back until they had made thousand-foot chasms through the mountains. The more southerly of these, when it reached the river in the central valley, beheaded it, leaving the Jordan in a small drainage area to the south and forming up above it the Litani, which now flows south for a short distance and then turns sharply west through the gorge to the Mediterranean. Farther north, when the other stream had cut through the mountains and reached the valley river, it took the whole upper end of that once-long, southward-flowing stream and reversed it, so that today the Orontes rises in the valley north of the headwaters of the Litani, flows north a little way, and then turns westward through a chasm into the sea.

Most rivers have had to carve out their basins not only at their heads but throughout their entire courses. Some of the giants among present-day rivers—the Amazon and the Congo, among others—flow in natural basins formed by other geologic forces, but the direction and extent of the majority of streams, as well as the size and shape of their drainage areas, have been determined by the erosive work of the rivers themselves.

As they gradually lower their basins and reduce their gradients, rivers smooth out irregularities in their courses. Striking into a depression, for example, water will pond up until it finds a place where the new-made lake can overflow. Through this lake the river may pass for a long age, as the Rhone is at present flowing through Lake Geneva. But gradually it fills in the upper end with sediment and cuts the outlet deeper and deeper until eventually it is left flowing directly across the dry bed of the former lake.

Chiefly, the work of rivers is destructive: the great primeval alterations were brought about by the ceaseless attack on the rocks, the breaking and stripping off, the slow eating away, the chemical action that corroded and softened and disintegrated—all that sawed canyons and scooped out valleys, all that humbled the mountains and brought them low. This work was done for the most part at the heads of the streams, and to a lesser extent along their courses. As a destructive agent, a river is more effective the faster it flows; whenever it slows sufficiently it ceases to tear down and begins to build. This may happen anywhere along its course, but is most noticeable at its mouth, when it is finally halted by the sluggish mass of the sea. There the silt that is still suspended in the water settles, and spreads out in smooth layers on the ocean floor. The layers of sediment slowly pack and harden into new kinds of rock, which may, eons later, be thrust up to form mountains again and high plateaus. When rivers disencumber themselves of the burden gravity and velocity have laid upon them, they build in their deltas new land forms from the debris of those they have destroyed.

At one time in the geologic past, a huge continent extended over the area now covered by the North Atlantic Ocean, its eastern edges sloping down to points in what are now the British Isles. For seventy-five million years, great rivers flowed down that sloping continent, carrying particles of sand stripped off, grain by grain, from hot mountains far in the west and laying them down in deep strata (the so-called "Old Red Sandstone") on the floor of the ocean. In time, those deltaic strata were lifted into what we call the Scottish Highlands. They were eventually quarried: in the walls of many a Scottish abbey the remembered heat of Atlantean deserts still faintly glows. Farther south along the coast of Atlantis, where other rivers brought down dark and glistening mud instead of sand, sedimentary deposits formed the Cornish slates. These, too, have been dug by men, who have used them for the more humble purpose of making roofs.

When the continent of Atlantis had subsided and the British Isles were part of the European land mass, a huge anonymous river flowing from Scandinavia down into northern England entered a warm sea and deposited its burden of coarse, gritty pebbles in a fanlike delta. When river and sea and time had transformed this debris into a stratum of indestructibly ugly stone, it was heaved up into the Pennine Hills. Nineteenth-century builders found it, called it by the appropriately harsh name of "millstone grit," and built of it such enduring monuments as Euston Station in London and the Bradford waterworks.

In the shaping of the earth as we know it, earth forms built by rivers have been less significant, on the whole,

23

than the alterations caused by their destructive action. Yet some deltas have had considerable importance. The Gulf of Mexico, one of whose bays once reached up to the present site of St. Louis, was pushed southward nearly a thousand miles by deposits from primeval rivers. Geologists hold that the Mississippi Valley, at least the part southward from the confluence with the Ohio, owes its extraordinary fertility to the fact that it is made of silt, just as it owes its very existence to the archaic rivers that laid it down. The great plain of northern India, in which cultivable topsoil extends downward in places as much as five hundred feet, has been similarly built by the rivers streaming down from the Himalayas. One of the richest agricultural areas in the world, the whole Gangetic basin is a huge trough which the rivers have filled with the life-giving soil of denuded mountains. Within historic time, the Tigris and Euphrates, which formerly entered the Persian Gulf through separate mouths, have extended their converging beds until they met, and have continued to lay down land on either side of their common channel, so that the sites of ancient ports are now many miles inland from the gulf. They are still increasing the land area of Iraq, pushing back the sea at a steady rate of 160 feet every year. In the same way the land area of China has grown through the ages, helped especially by rivers like the Yellow (Hwang Ho), which often carries a weight of suspended solids greater than the weight of the water itself.

The building of earth forms that are useful to men is not confined to deltaic deposits. Wherever the flood plain of a river is only very slightly tilted, the raging water at each inundation is slowed down when it overflows its banks and fertile silt is spread evenly over the soil. The flood plain and delta of the Nile are the only cultivable part of Egypt; the rest is not merely dry desert but it also lacks the nutrients that make the silt-covered areas so fertile. Rivers like the Yellow have built up their beds higher than the surrounding plains; when they flood, they cause enormous destruction, but they also leave the fields richer than they were before.

Like all things else, rivers are subject to accident. In the northern hemisphere, many features of the landscape we see today are the result of cataclysmic accidents suffered by rivers during the Ice Ages. Before the ice sheets bore down upon North America, for example, the Ohio River did not exist. The Allegheny and Monongahela, whose junction today marks the beginning of the Ohio, were at that time northward-flowing streams which emptied into the St. Lawrence system. Rain falling on the southwest of their watershed found its way down into an enormous river geologists now call the Teays. This stream rose in the mountains near present-day Blowing Rock, North Carolina, flowed in a general northwesterly direction across Virginia, West Virginia, and Ohio, then turned west across Indiana and Illinois, and finally emptied into the Gulf of Mexico through a channel that is now used by the Illinois River. The descent of the ice sheets completely altered the drainage patterns of that whole area. Blocked by ice barriers, the Monongahela and Allegheny halted, filled their basins, and overflowed into the Teays, completely reversing their direction and that of some of their tributaries. But below that new junction, the Teays itself was blocked by the same ice sheets pushing southeastward from the Great Lakes region. Part of its waters, plus those added by the new tributaries, cut a new bed along the southern edge of the ice and poured into the bay that was to become the Mississippi Valley, thus forming the present Ohio River. But not all the water in the Teays was turned aside into the new bed; a considerable part of it continued to flow in

25

its original gravel bed, pushed down under millions of tons of ice. Buried alive, the Teays still lives and flows, deep under the layers of glacial soil left on top of it when the ice melted, and it supplies thousands of wells to farms and towns in the Middle West.

In the successive periods of intense cold, scores of rivers were impounded by the ice sheets and turned into strange courses. The Ob and the Yenisei, unable any longer to reach the Arctic Ocean, spread out over the Siberian plain in the largest lake that has ever existed on the earth. It remained a fresh-water lake because it eventually over-flowed to the south and the water could drain into the Caspian depression; unable to find an outlet from there, it formed a salt sea. When the ice finally melted, the outlet towards the Caspian ceased to flow because it was at a higher elevation than the old beds of Ob and Yenisei, and so the great lake finally drained away through their liberated channels. Recently, men have decided that it might be useful to re-create the enormous lake by damming the Ob, in order to divert Siberian river-water southwest once again, through the Aral Sea and into the Caspian. Such a project, if it were carried out, would create the largest man-made waterway in the world, and would also furnish irrigation for great deserts now useless. Thus a onetime accident of nature might be duplicated consciously and for definite purposes.

Where small remnants of the Ice Age linger, the purposeless accident still happens occasionally to rivers, though on nothing like the same scale. In 1926, the Little Khumdan glacier, which from time immemorial had perched high up in the Himalayas in a tributary valley above the gorge of the Shyok River, slipped and plunged into the gorge, forming an ice dam behind which the blocked stream began to build up into a lake. In August

1928, when the lake had grown to be nine miles long and more than half a mile wide, the ice dam began to crack. Panic seized the villages and towns along the river banks below: if the ice gave way, and the whole lake were poured suddenly into the bed, the resulting flood would sweep down the valleys into the Indus, and all human beings and their works along that vast river might be swirled headlong into the sea. Villages were hurriedly evacuated; a system of beacon signals was arranged to give warning all down the twisting valleys, where the light, leaping from hill to hill, could outrun the rushing water. While the ice was still groaning against the combined pressures of gravity, a wandering caravan in the mountains camped one night and built a fire to cook their meals, and when its light was seen in the distant valleys the terror of threatened humanity emptied yet more villages.

But as things turned out, the ice dam did not break to release a flood. Instead, the struggling waters of the Shyok at length dug an opening under the great bulk of the glacier, and began to drain harmlessly down their former bed. The remnant of the Little Khumdan glacier is still there in the gorge, but people in the lower valleys have long since returned to their daily affairs, using their liberated river as calmly as if an ice mountain had never fallen across its path and made it temporarily a lake capable of taking them into oblivion.

Accidents accounted for some of the land forms created by the earliest rivers, but most of the changes that gradually converted the sheer rock into land, with its infinite variety of soils and shapes, were the result of the normal flow of water. What rounded the sharp peaks and ground them down, what sawed the gorges, widened the valleys, filled the lakes, and built the deltas was just water making its witless way to the sea. Although that process goes steadily on, it proceeds so slowly by human reckoning that it is not apparent. Men came at first into what seemed a completed universe, and only comparatively recently have they discovered through what vast stretches of time the rivers have been making the world habitable.

All the shifting and changing of primordial rivers, all those gigantic scourings and dumpings, transpired in unimaginable silence because there was no ear to hear and in darkness inconceivable because there was no eye to see. Consciousness awoke in a world already incredibly ancient, where long-vanished rivers had time and again carried forgotten continents into unrecorded seas, and where no conscious act had ever challenged the undirected processes of creation and destruction. Men have learned, it is true, to make good use of what the rivers built. They have taken the residues of petrified deltas for their masonry as blithely as a bird, pecking in the gravel of a suburban pathway, may take a particle of some vanished Himalaya to grind the seeds in its craw. But what the archaic rivers carried to the sea was not Euston Station or the roof of a cow barn, but only the bone-flake and ash of dying mountains. When the accumulated rubbish dropped from the rivers' grasp there were no human hands to take it. The constructions of men, now that hands have been evolved, are the result of a mass of shared and communicated experience, made possible by men's peculiar ability to think, to learn, to experiment, to plan, and to co-operate.

The story of men's dealings with rivers is the story of the intrusion of consciousness into an insentient universe. It is one phase of the great drama in which the human mind is forever pitted against mindless force. Every use men have made of rivers, every advance in science and technical skill as applied to water resources, has been the result of a pitched battle between an insubstantial thought and the massive indifference of senseless matter. It is a drama whose scenes have occurred in a recognizable order, one following the other in a reasonably logical progression. The discoveries and inventions that have made possible each new episode are fairly well documented and the results are generally known. But this step-by-step development of men's ability to control and manage rivers is by no means the whole story.

For a history of any branch of technology implies a history of humanity in general. Discoveries may be important in themselves, but what makes them significant for human beings is that they bring changes in men's ways of living, in the way they organize their communal affairs, in their ideas of what is right and what is wrong, in their attitudes towards other human beings and towards the world they live in. A paleolithic (Old Stone Age) culture, in which the tools are made of stones rather crudely chipped and shaped by being hit with other stones, has one set of characteristics; when people learn to make better tools by grinding and polishing the stones, their whole culture undergoes such a revolution that we must use another name, neolithic (New Stone Age), to describe it. The later Bronze Age cultures differ even more remarkably, and the still later use of iron brings again revolutionary changes that affect the whole society. The most familiar example of a new technology producing an entirely new social organization is the Industrial Revolution. Even more far-reaching were the consequences of early men's discovery that they could control and increase their food supply by cultivating plants and domesticating animals. In all the later stages of our development, every improvement in food-getting tools has had its social results.

What we may not have realized quite so clearly is that water, which is just as essential to human life as food, has played an equally decisive role. The story of men's relations with rivers can tell us as much about the evolution of

29

society as the story of the land and the food men take from it. The first diversion of river water through an artificial channel is a landmark of equal importance with the first scythe or the first cattle corral; the first ride in a wheeled cart drawn by oxen was no more spectacular or crucial than the first trip in a boat, which had occurred far earlier. The conscious attempt to conserve water against a time of drought is as sure an indication of forethought, resulting from innumerable scientific observations and logical deductions, as the storage of grain for the next year's planting. And assuredly, such inventions as dams and water mills are as revolutionary as the plow: their consequences have, in fact, been infinitely greater.

The stages by which men achieved such mastery over rivers as they now have, and the resultant changes in human society, form the basic framework of the story. But rivers have meant more in human experience than this. From the beginning, they have drawn men into settlements, and then tempted them to expand those groupings into larger unities. They fostered men's earliest desires to trade their surpluses with other men, and they still carry an enormous proportion of the goods that are moved about the world. As men have wandered restlessly over the physical planet, rivers have been their guides into the unknown lands. As image and symbol, they have provided clues to the final mysteries of that insubstantial universe which the mind of man never tires of exploring.

All these relationships, and many more, are especially meaningful today. We live in a time when rivers and what we may do with them are more important than ever before. More work is being done, and it is work of greater immediate significance to more people. As a result of recent developments, the enormous potential of the river is, for nation after nation, the most positive reason they have for facing the future with hope and courage. That potential is one of the central facts which must be taken into account in any attempt to understand how far humanity has come, where it is going, and what we who live in this century ought to be doing.

What men have done in the past they have often done without any very clear plan, and without guessing at the eventual consequences. But from their history as a whole, a pattern emerges. Whether men intended it or not, their drama as they have enacted it has an order and a progression in it, and moves towards a goal. In their dealings with rivers, they have revealed not only their nature but their ultimate intentions. There are of course many setbacks, many distortions, many accidents. Men have been passionate, selfish, willful, and on occasions downright silly, and all these weaknesses have at times made them stumble and slide back. Although they have always spent the bulk of their energies in plain hard work, they have used up so much of the remainder in fighting with each other that some historians have thought quarreling and killing their basic incentives. But their story, when we look at it closely, reveals the persistence of an urge that is more deeply and permanently rooted in humanity than the fighting instinct. It is the instinct to co-operate, to seek ways of establishing with other men a sense of community, an assurance and fulfillment of their common humanity.

Whatever the motives that may at any moment have prompted it, however inadequate or cruel or absurd the means may sometimes have been, the search for community runs through human history as clearly as a river runs through its course from mountain to sea. "Growth and progress," as Pandit Nehru has observed, "consist in co-operation between larger and larger units." In their relations with rivers, men have made progress, and they have grown.

CHAPTER II

The Savage by the Stream

WHEN they first appeared in the world, men gave little indication of the role they would eventually play. Consciousness was barely awake in them, making them unready to challenge the blind forces of nature any more effectively than other animals do. They were notoriously feeble, these awkward creatures who stood almost upright on two legs only and had no tail to use for a third balance point. There was little about their physical make-up to suggest that they were destined to meddle with nature, to interfere with the downward flow of her waters, turning them this way and that into unaccustomed channels and even enslaving them in whirling turbines in order to draw off (through absurdly thin wires) some portion of their massive power.

For the first several hundred thousand years of their existence, our remotest ancestors were so little able to affect their environment that modern anthropologists, who see human beings as essentially makers and changers, are reluctant to call them "men" at all; they usually prefer the term "hominids," manlike creatures, for all the species who preceded *Homo sapiens*. Even when genuine men appeared, fully evolved and perfected, they seemed as little likely to succeed as any organism the evolutionary process had so far produced. Lacking claws and fangs, slow in movement, without scales for armor or horns for fighting, thin-skinned, and not well adapted for swimming or burrowing, they were forced to depend for survival on the few characteristics in which they excelled all other forms of life: brains, eyes, and hands.

Because they had big, complex, intricately co-ordinated brains, they were able to control the fire from which all other animals fled in terror. Eyes that could focus, producing a single vision of an object instead of a double one, and hands that are more delicately adjusted than the appendages of any other creature—these, directed by the brain, could produce tools. The reason we know that men lived on this earth at many times and in many places from which their bones have vanished is that we have found the stones they chipped to make a cutting edge. Such stones could dig more effectively than human fingernails; they could strike a heavier and sharper blow than the human fist; and they could be hurled to bring down an animal far beyond the reach of a human arm.

Even with this equipment, men were so nearly helpless in the primeval world that the most improbable fact in their history is that they survived at all. From the very beginning, their survival was intimately related to the rivers they were eventually to master. There was no mastery at first; the relationship was one of complete and utter dependence on the part of men. They were bound to the river as squirrels are bound to nut-bearing forests, for it was the only source they knew of the sweet water which

33

they must drink in order to live. That is why, if you set out today to search for traces of your remotest ancestors, you must go, as they went, to the rivers. There may be no flowing water there today, but the gravels where you are likely to find the most primitive stone implements are in terraces that mark the abandoned beds of ancient rivers. Caves are another likely spot, but the caves where men lived were always along the sides of valleys through which the water flowed. They could not be anywhere else. Lacking any means of carrying water with them on their wanderings, early men were forced to keep within walking distance of the natural sources.

The river bank was man's earliest home for another equally decisive reason. Men must eat as well as drink, and because the animals they prey upon are under the same compulsion to take the water where they find it, the margins of a stream were the most reliable hunting ground. Perhaps it was this function of the river as the summoner of game, the magnet that drew his food irresistibly to his hand, that made the deepest impression on man's slowly awakening mind. It is dangerous, of course, to speculate upon mental attitudes among peoples who had no way of recording their impressions of the world they lived in. But when, after thousands upon thousands of years of the hunting life, men at last discovered how to make "pictures" of their world, the first inanimate object they recorded from their environment is the edge of a river, and the only thing their picture tells us about this bit of landscape is that this is where one finds an edible animal. The object that gives us this first insight is a rounded piece of antler found at Kesslerloch in Switzerland, on which some paleolithic artist, twenty or twenty-five thousand years ago, scratched a very fine representation of a reindeer grazing along the banks of a stream. (PLATE 1)

It is curious and instructive to reflect that no other inanimate detail of the natural environment seems to have made any impression on the mind of primitive man. Men were artists, and great ones, for thousands of years before it ever occurred to anybody to represent a hill or a mountain, or to record anything at all of the way the world looked to him except this one glimpse of a river. The great paleolithic art of the European cave painter was rigidly practical; it was concerned primarily with the hunt, and to a much lesser extent with what may possibly have been some strange speculations about fertility. It took no notice of landscape as such, for that is an interest that springs from leisure and aesthetic sensibility, and the hunters of the Old Stone periods could not afford these luxuries. Yet there on the antler chip is the river clearly flowing, the reeds and sedges invading its shallows, and the grass beyond on which the reindeer feeds.

Naturally, animals would avoid the spots where the smell of man was heavy. Berries, grubs, and other foods had to be collected from wherever nature might place them, and this was not always at hand. Of necessity, people who depended for food on what they could find and capture could not sit down beside their river and wait. They were obliged to wander. But since they were also obliged to return to their lairs, they must have landmarks to guide them. The most obvious is the river itself, as it is also the most reliable. Hills and mountains are treacherously deceptive, all things visible in the sky are in constant movement, even one stone or one tree can look remarkably like another. But a river flows always in the same direction. For primitive men, it offered the surest means of finding their way home. From it they derived the first glimmerings of geographical knowledge.

This function of the river, as teacher of the elements of

geography, has persisted down to our own time. On the earliest map we know, a plan of Babylonia as it was conceived in the eighteenth century before Christ, the Euphrates is not merely the largest and most obvious detail; it is a huge slash extending from one point on the circular, all-enveloping ocean to the opposite point, bisecting the round disk of the known world: the central fact in the setting of the human drama. Through most of recorded history, rivers have retained this central role. (PLATE 2) When new coast lines have come into human ken, it is the harbors, the mouths of the great rivers, that have first been charted. By means of these rivers, explorers have always sought entry into the strange countries, and down the rivers again they have made good their escape when the new regions proved inhospitable. Until aircraft made it possible for men to survey a land on which they had never walked, there was only one safe highway into the unknown.

One would suppose that anything so vital to human existence would have been of absorbing interest to the human mind from its earliest awakening. Did primitive men realize, even dimly, how complete was their dependence, and did they try to do anything to minimize it? There is no evidence, but I think we may assume they did not, that they simply took the water in its natural courses for granted, as animals do. It was a fact of existence, like day and night; an absolute necessity, but one given freely by nature, requiring no effort on man's part.

As for any attempt to assert control over it, this was out of the question. When men conceive the possibility that nature may be controlled, but have not developed the necessary technology to do it, they generally resort to magic, to the pitiful hope that if they make a picture of the reindeer they need for food, an actual reindeer will materialize;

36

or that if they call them with religious poetry, the herds will come. At least as early as the later Ice Age, men in Europe were certainly attempting to control the supply of game and the fortunes of the chase by magical means. But it never occurred to them to apply their magic to the streams because they had no need to. For the same reason, it was millennia later, after men living alongside quite different rivers had developed a way of life which the river could completely destroy, before anyone thought of deifying it, of worshiping it as a god or placating it as a terrifying demon. It is possible that the food-gathering cave artists may have seen floods, and may have been momentarily frightened, but as long as there were still animals to be killed and eaten, and berries and roots to be collected, there was no reason for any mystical ideas to arise.

I have suggested that the earliest men had no vessels in which they could store water, or even carry it. This is not positively established; what we must say is that they made no vessels of any material that has lasted long enough for us to identify them. The cave artists of the so-called "upper paleolithic" societies that flourished in Europe at the end of the Ice Age had small, saucer-like stones for holding some kind of fatty substance. They used these objects for lamps, presumably to lighten the blackness of the caves where their decorations occur. There is nothing that looks like a vessel to hold any other liquid, except, on some very early sites, a few human skulls that have been hacked into crude drinking cups. Whether they ever used a piece of curved bark or a hollow bone for such a purpose is a matter for speculation only. Some kinds of water containers are quite within the possibilities open to savage societies, of course: we know that in other parts of the world people at a similar stage of development have used gourds, ostrich eggs, hollow bamboo sections, animal skins

37

and organs, and a wide variety of other objects requiring only the simplest manufacturing skills. But precisely what paleolithic Europeans used we do not know. Surely when a man fell ill his comrades must either have carried him down to the stream or have contrived some way of bringing water to him. Cool water to drink and to bathe fevered bodies was certainly the earliest substance for the treatment of illness, and must for long have remained the only one. When medicine at length became a science, it owed as much to the ancient concern with springs and healing waters, with purification rites and the great medley of superstition and sense about water in general, as to any other source; and the river as the source of pure drinking water is still one of the principal concerns of the most advanced public health authorities.

One wonders much about the life of savage men, hunting along the banks of the rivers they could never leave for long. Did they splash in the water, and discover that it could be a source of pure pleasure, to say nothing of cleanliness? Contemporary savages wash their clothes in streams, but their earliest prototypes had no clothes to wash. It seems likely that if they lived in a warm climate they must have bathed, and equally likely that where their streams trickled out from under the glaciers they did not. Say the word "river" to a city dweller today and there is a high probability that the first images which will flash through his mind will be of a place of recreation. But if he were a nearly helpless savage, compelled to focus almost his entire energies on the hunt for food, it is not certain that the idea of swimming for pleasure would ever occur to him. There are many other questions about the possible relationship between prehistoric men and their rivers which there is no point in our asking because there is no possible way of answering them.

Certain vital matters, however, are known. There is no doubt, for example, that paleolithic savages made one discovery about rivers that was of the greatest importance, both immediately and in its later consequences. Exactly when and where and by whom the discovery was made we do not know, but the earliest proof that it had been made is in various caves in France, and seems to have been left there some fifteen thousand years ago.

For a very long period before that time, people with extraordinary mental abilities had been living in various parts of Europe. Like all other human beings at that time, they were hunters, who had not yet dreamed of controlling their food supply by taming animals or plants. But they had developed the hunting economy to a far higher level than it had reached before. For one thing, they used the earliest machines of which we have any record: the spear thrower and the bow and arrow. The brilliance of their achievement as machine makers is indicated by the fact that the mechanical principles employed in these tools remained the most effective any men could devise for weapons of warfare and the hunt right down to the advent of gunpowder.

The most remarkable thing about these people, however, is that consciousness had awakened in them to an unprecedented degree; they could record their experience as human beings in a hostile environment, and some of those records are works of very fine art. On cave walls and on pieces of bone and antler, they made pictures of the animals on whose bodies they fed. From these pictures, we know that they were in Europe when the Ice Age was just ending and there was still an almost glacial climate, for the earliest of their engravings and drawings depict mammoths and woolly rhinoceroses. Because succeeding generations frequently made new pictures over earlier ones

39

left by their ancestors, we can see that they stayed on as the climate grew warmer and arctic beasts were replaced by animals of the tundra and steppe, of the later evergreen forest, and of the still later mixed hardwood forest: bison, wild horses, reindeer, and finally forest deer and cattle.

Their art, and their general culture, reached its highest development (what is called the Magdalenian phase) at the time when the reindeer were abundant. Thousands of pieces of antler were etched with fine skill, and in hundreds of caves the walls of the deepest chambers were decorated with masterpieces of vigorous, realistic painting: frenzied horses falling over cliffs; great bulls angrily tossing their horns; a bison surprised by the hunter, nervously pawing the ground as he stands in an agony of indecision whether to charge or to run away; and everywhere the lordly reindeer, the mainstay of the human economy.

At the height of the Magdalenian, the artists quite suddenly introduced a new subject into the record of their prey. They began to draw, with just as fine skill and from equally close observation, the outlines of salmon that came on their annual migrations fighting their way up the Dordogne River to their spawning grounds, and of trout that inhabited the swift streams of the Pyrenees. From this time forward, fish abound in paleolithic art, as one can see from consulting the enormous catalogue drawn up by the Abbé Breuil, to whom we owe the greater part of our knowledge of this subject. The meaning of these drawings and engravings is evident: the river had become a source of food. (Plate 3)

It is an event in the human story of more than ordinary interest, for it marks not only a great advance in technical skill and a change in the economic basis of life, but a stage in the development of the human consciousness as well. The minds that first directed the capture of fish had gone through a process that represents a formidable amount of scientific observation, delicacy and skill in toolmaking, and profound thought. Driving mammoths or wild horses over cliffs is crude animal behavior compared with the silent art of fishing. It is not surprising that some authorities believe so subtle a craft originated in a period when game was abundant; in other words, that it came as the result of a certain amount of leisure, and was the product not so much of grim necessity as of curiosity and speculation.

The results of the introduction of fishing are no less impressive. For thousands of years men had depended for the essential proteins on the flesh of animals. They had been forced to wander, following the herds but always coming back to the water without which they could not live. Now they had discovered that the water itself could furnish a staple food. And once the streams were added to the land as a possible hunting ground, men's chances of survival were immeasurably increased. The addition of fish to the diet must have had a wholesome effect on the health of the community. And if the herds were depleted by over-hunting or disease, or if they simply wandered away, men could still eat and live. In fact, to appreciate just how much this extension of control over the natural environment has meant to humanity, one has only to reflect that fishing is almost the only example of pure food gathering which is still practiced in our highly complex, industrialized, food-producing economy, as an essential enterprise for feeding the human family. There is only one other sizable food industry which still depends on the natural supply; and whale hunting, which grew out of fishing, is of very minor importance by comparison.

New crafts require new tools, and from the time when fish appear in paleolithic art the weapons of the fisherman exist side by side with those of the hunter. Through the changing forms of the tackle, we can trace a growing awareness of the importance of the new industry and a consequent refinement in all the skills needed for its pursuit. The fish spear, made of bone, was replaced fairly early by the far more sophisticated harpoon, with a detachable head fashioned from reindeer antler. It is a better weapon, for it can be thrown from the hand and retrieved, whereas the spear must be held. It is also harder to produce. To make these harpoon heads, heavily barbed by cutting deep incisions into the hard material, requires very careful workmanship, and one needs considerable knowledge of ties in order to fasten them securely to the shafts. Furthermore, the harpooner must have more patience and a finer muscular co-ordination than the spear thrower needs.

Finally, men who had found this vast new source of food and were determined to exploit it to the limit of their abilities devised one of the subtlest of all snares. The harpoon, for all its superiority over the fixed spear, has one serious limitation: it is useless unless the harpooner can see the target he wants to hit. And men must soon have discovered that fish have a way of darting suddenly, just as the harpoon leaves the hand, into depths where the water makes them invisible. Goaded by such frustration, they were driven to invent a weapon that could pursue the elusive game into its hiding place, entice it to impale itself on the very barb it fled from, hold it fast against the frantic power of its death agony, and finally bring it back to the waiting hand.

It was a formidable problem, and if we knew what man had solved it by inventing a baited hook upon a line we should doubtless enroll him among the great scientists who are his peers. He is nameless, of course, but he may have belonged to that same brilliant society of Europeans in the Magdalenian phase, for among their artifacts have been found some little straight bone bars, sharpened into a point at either end, which may have been the first fishhooks. They do not look very efficient, but it does seem that if a fish took one in his mouth it would catch crosswise in his gullet; and since the archaeologists cannot think of any other use these objects might have had it is assumed that this was their purpose.

There is no indication that people in the Magdalenian phase made any further advances in the fishing industry, nor that they had any inkling of the next great step men were to take in the use of rivers. They had exploited their bleak environment almost as fully as it is possible to do within the severe limitations of an economy based entirely on food gathering. One further step in river use was to be taken before the whole economic basis of human society was radically altered, but the Magdalenians did not take it. For one thing, the climate was against them. It was all right as long as the ice sheets were not too far north of them, but gradually the southern edges were melting as warmer air came slowly up from the south. Tundra had been succeeded by steppe, and then by forest; mammoths and woolly rhinoceroses had gone away into the north and finally died, and as the warmth increased still more, even the reindeer retreated from southern Europe, taking with them the supply of antler for fine harpoons. Fish still swarmed in the rivers, but it was harder to make good tackle for capturing them, for the antlers of the forest deer who were now plentiful were spongy at the core and had to be split before deep-cut barbs could be made, which meant that men must be contented with smaller and weaker harpoon heads. The fishing industry declined, and eventually the supply itself fell off as the fish sought colder waters, fewer and fewer salmon returning on their annual migrations to the old spawning beds.

The drama of the savage by the stream was not played out to the end, however, for there were still unexhausted possibilities within a hunting, collecting way of life. People who fished as well as hunted could, and did, make a number of developments beyond what the Magdalenians had achieved. For example, in the peat bogs of Denmark and other northern countries archaeologists have found evidence that fishermen living around the lakes and streams in those parts some eight thousand years before the Christian era were making not only fish spears and harpoons, but real fishhooks as well. They even attached bark floats onto fish nets, which they made of plant fibers. Probably similar tackle was made in many other parts of the world where there were no peat bogs to preserve it for our inspection.

Finally, the relics of these north European fishermen show the beginnings of an extremely important development in the relationship between rivers and people. By their time, the river had become the first of all the natural forces which have been made to perform useful work for men. We know that these people had boats, for the peat bogs have yielded up the wooden paddles they used to propel them. On various rocks and dolmens, men living the same kinds of lives at later periods scratched stylized pictures of these vessels, some large enough to carry fourteen men.

Whether these people were the very first to use the river as a bearer of burdens is an academic question. It will not do to be dogmatic about when and where the first boat was made, nor to speculate very much about whether it was a European log hollowed out by chipping and firing, or a bundle of African reeds lashed together to make a raft, both of which were quite possibly preceded by inflated skin floats or bark canoes; the archaeological information is still too meager. But it would be difficult to overestimate the significance of man's discovery of the buoyancy of water; of his observation that although a stone will sink, a lightweight log will not, and neither will a stone placed upon a log. Dozens of men may sweat and strain to lift a great boulder, or to shove it along the ground. Once it is safely loaded onto a boat, a child can tow it along the shore or the river unaided can carry it downstream. When men had found this out, they had taken the first step on the long road that leads to emancipation from physical drudgery.

It is usually said that animals and the wind were men's first servants, but though this assertion is made confidently by many authorities it would seem to need some qualification. Certainly the domestication of animals and the use of their greater muscular power for hauling and carrying did make it possible for men to do things they could never have done with their own puny muscles, just as the wind could propel a boat faster and with less effort than a set of oars could when men learned how to catch the wind's power in a sail. But rivers had carried men and their burdens for many long centuries before either of these other servants was employed.

If I labor the point, it is not for the sake of a mere quibble over priority. Until men saw some natural force actually doing the work they wanted done, they could not dream that it was possible to be freed from physical labor, to be stronger than their own bodies, to assert their control over forces which had always seemed dominant and hostile. They never saw wild animals pulling or carrying anything, and it never occurred to them that these animals could be made to do such things until centuries of use of the river's carrying power had taught them that such a shifting of the burden might be possible. But from their earliest observations they had seen the streams carrying past their settlements all manner of flotsam. Man's dream of himself as a free agent, creating the shape of his own environment by the imposition of his will, has been the spur that has urged him on to all his later endeavors and achievements. And that dream was born in the mind of the savage beside the stream.

Boats and rafts opened the way for the large-scale transfer of goods, the trade that was to be the lifeblood of later societies. Once they had been launched, men had embarked on the journey whose end is not yet in sight. Stonehenge would arise on Salisbury Plain, Solomon would buy from Hiram the towering cedars that could lift up the praise of God on Mount Zion, and Egyptian ladies would paint their eyelids with the green malachite from mines upriver in Nubia. Through succeeding ages, the river has never been displaced as an avenue of trade and commerce. At the command of men, it has carried a greater load of material goods than all the highroads. This has come about because men in the most primitive stage of their social evolution learned that rivers can be made to submit their broad backs to the burdens we place upon them.

For some of these extremely early societies, rivers assumed the function of defensive barriers, antedating and no doubt suggesting all the later elaboration of man-made moats and military canals. Some of the more dangerous wild animals will not swim in pursuit of prey, but only as a last desperate means of escape when they are the intended victims. If a primitive hunter could put a stream between himself and a tiger, he was reasonably safe. In the same way, a river gave a certain amount of protection, on one side of his encampment at least, from attack by human enemies. Islands in a large river or lake were of course even more easily defended, and it was not long before men learned to make artificial islands of logs or mud-and-brushwood to which they could retire in emergencies; such man-made island fortresses have been found among the northern lake dwellers, in Switzerland, in marshy sections of England, and elsewhere; they represent the earliest attempts at civil engineering. We shall see that this role of the river as shield, elaborated and developed in countless ingenious ways, has persisted as a cardinal factor in military tactics right down to the present, when airplanes have not yet made tanks and infantrymen obsolete.

By the time the boats were afloat, human society was drawing near one of the greatest transformations it has ever undergone. Food-gathering savagery was soon to be replaced as the universal pattern of human existence by forms of social organization rooted in an infinitely richer and more secure economy. It would persist, but as a dying organism; the progress of man required conditions which it could never create, and one by one the more forward-looking peoples abandoned it. Today it exists precariously only on the backward fringes.

Men who had no way of feeding themselves except to hunt and collect what nature happened to provide could achieve, at most, only a very limited degree of freedom. Tied to the natural watercourses because they had no ability to alter drainage patterns or to tap the waters under the earth, they lived in such intimate dependence on their rivers that to us it seems bondage. Yet though mastery was out of the question, they had already learned to use, in some ways, what they could not hope to control.

How much they had actually learned about the water that flowed past their settlements is an open question. Did they discover some of its basic characteristics, which later men were to use in all sorts of industrial processes? Human beings did not find out what water actually is until

47

around A.D. 1783, when Cavendish, Watt, and Lavoisier all reached the conclusion that it contained about two parts of hydrogen to one part of oxygen, and the accurate chemical analysis of water came later still. By that time, many of the useful, practical facts about it had been common knowledge for millennia. All those facts, however, had once been unknown, and it is sobering to reflect that we owe certain of them to the sharp, inquisitive minds of our savage ancestors.

Paleolithic men, for example, knew that water mixed with certain muds would produce a substance that could be molded and worked, and that when the water had dried out the substance would hold its shape. Clay was the first plastic, and gave men their first inkling that they could control a physical change from liquid to semiliquid to solid. In the cave of Les Trois Frères in the Pyrenees there are large clay figures of bison, modeled in almost full relief, and clay figurines are fairly common in paleolithic art. But this fundamental discovery was apparently not used to make pots or building-bricks until much later, when the whole mode of human life was changing. In any work with clay, however, it is necessary to wash out the grits in order to produce a smooth and malleable plastic, so that the primitive artists must have discovered the basic principle of most of the elaborate separation processes required in modern industry.

In a society where water and animal grease are virtually the only known liquids, it is inevitable that people will learn all sorts of uses for both. The ability of water to quench fire must have been known as early as fire handling itself, and some knowledge of its uses as a coolant must be equally ancient. But one wonders whether people who were always working with flint did not discover that if cold water is thrown on a heated rock, the rock will split. It is

48

a method that was used by later miners, but there is no way of knowing how early it was found out. Similarly, the whole complex business of soaking skins to make them pliable, and later of using water in the intricate processes of extracting fibers from plants and preparing them for plaiting or weaving both represent vital contributions to human development. When such a remarkable discovery as the processing of textile fibers was first made we do not know, but it was certainly before the time when fish nets were left in the Danish peat bog.

There were two achievements of savage society, however, that were to mean as much for the future as any we have discussed. When later men have undertaken to tame the great rivers of the world, to lift them bodily from their beds and drive them through unnatural channels where they may do men's bidding, two things have always been required for success. One is the ability of men to work together, in larger and larger groups. Prehistoric savages did not apply teamwork to such things as irrigation projects, of course, but they did build up a tribal organization and thus laid the foundations for future large-scale co-operation. Success in hunting the great beasts on whose bodies they fed required the co-ordinated work of a far larger group of people than the single family. Magical rites and initiations are group activities, and the development of schools of art, which we believe existed in Magdalenian cultures, presupposes a great deal of social organization, as well as the pooling and handing on of masses of collective knowledge. The men who eventually took the rivers in hand were already inheritors of a long tradition of co-operation and social discipline.

The other essential in all successful river work is a mental attitude. Men do not master their environment until they have first conceived the notion that mastery is possible. It

49

appears that this exhilarating idea had occurred to the cave painters and formed part of their spiritual legacy to later men. In the same cave that contains the clay bison, there is one of their few representations of a human figure; engraved and painted with great care and considerable artistic power, it depicts a man engaged in a ceremonial dance. On the head are stag's horns; the face is an owl's, with wolf ears and a beard; there seems to be a fur-covered skin hanging down the back and over the arms, with bear paws where the hands should be and a horsetail swinging under the lifted human leg. Here, in other words, is an abstract representation of man, endowed with the most potent weapons, senses, and skills of the lower creatures. We may say it is only magic, mere wishful thinking, but it is nevertheless a vision of man as a superior creature, a celebration of his unique power to outwit and to dominate. Man, having glimpsed the potential within himself, has begun the dance of conscious and purposive control over all the powers of nature, the dance of the lord of creation.

Such a moment of exaltation can come only after great achievement, when even greater accomplishments are foreshadowed. But those further advances could not be made by men who had to depend for their food on whatever they were able to find. For these people, the river could be landmark, source of food, and bearer of burdens; the river could form an effective barrier against certain kinds of marauding animals and sometimes a defense against human enemies. If it was infested with dangerous reptiles or man-eating fish, like some of the tropical rivers along whose banks savages still live, it could be extraordinarily dangerous. Above all, it was the source of the water which was just as necessary as food. Apart from establishing these rather simple relationships, there was little that primitive people could do; more complex ideas and interdependencies could arise only in the very different kind of society that was soon to evolve.

Savage society did not disappear from the earth when some members of the human family emerged from it into a less primitive way of life. But as the newer ways were adopted by more and more groups, those who clung to the simpler tribal organizations appropriate to a food-gathering economy were gradually pushed off the center of the stage. They continued to exist, as they still do, but because their lives are less interesting than those lived by other people they have long since given up their role as the central figures in the human story.

They can live only in a region where there are plentiful supplies of wild game or fish, or both, supplemented if possible by wild fruits and cereals or other edible plants. Their numbers are rigidly limited by the amount of food a natural environment can supply; they must therefore always live as a small population thinly spread over a very large area. In the same way, their home must be an area where natural water supplies are so abundant that they can neither pollute nor exhaust them. River valleys which can support a food-gathering people are becoming rare. Some exist along the northern fringes of North America, Europe, and Asia, but the various Eskimo tribes are dying out, squeezed into progressively smaller and leaner hunting grounds by the pressure of more advanced peoples moving up from the south, and their only hope of survival lies in their gradual adoption of some form of food production, such as reindeer breeding, to supplement the game bag. The great tributaries of the upper Amazon, flowing down through unexplored jungles where natural food products are incredibly abundant, are another haven of savage existence; so are a number of smaller river basins

51

in the less-known parts of Africa and Asia, and a few well-watered islands mostly in the Pacific and Indian oceans. In such regions, food gatherers can live, and within the stringent limits of ignorance, disease, and terror they can live reasonably well. But in most of them far larger populations of food producers could live better, and since we in the rest of the world have reached a stage where bad management has produced widespread poverty, the eyes of a hungry world are hopefully scanning these dark outposts. The days of the savage by these wild streams are numbered; sooner or later he will have to make the great economic change that other peoples made thousands of years ago or give way to those who will do it in his place. What will happen to his rivers and to his relationship with them can best be predicted by examining what has happened on other rivers in the past when savagery has been replaced by food-producing barbarism and later by civilization.

CHAPTER III

Ditches and Dams

W H E N men began to cultivate plants and to domesticate animals, their relationship with the rivers of the planet underwent some fundamental changes. This is not surprising, for the agricultural revolution has long been recognized as the most thoroughgoing of all the many changes men have made in the economics of living. Like all such changes, it altered the whole structure of society. Men who can produce their own food, who have found ways to plan and control the supply and to increase it at will, cannot continue to live as they did when survival depended on wandering herds and the chance discovery of wild berries or edible roots. Weapons and charms that were useful to the hunter fail miserably when the object is to milk a cow, and an uncontrolled salmon stream is not of much assistance to a farmer whose crops need rain. For the sake of a dependable supply of food, men had to alter the entire range of their thinking and activity. With their rivers they had to establish new relationships that could foster and enhance the new economy.

Up to a point, the rivers themselves conditioned the emergence of food production as the dominant way of life, simply by being the kinds of rivers men could easily adapt to their new requirements, or by failing to be. The cold and boisterous streams of the Pyrenees were suitable for fishing; postglacial meres and bogs, fed by trickles from the melting ice sheets, could foster the arts and crafts of the forest folk. But for security in the new kind of life men needed older rivers, rivers already grown wide and slow and half tamed, moving as placidly as oxen down the long monotony of sunlit plains until they lost themselves in the reeds and ooze of the swamp. Though cultivation seems to have arisen first in hill country somewhere in the Middle East, the great achievements of the barbarian village society it produced were made in the valleys and the broad, steamy deltas of rivers like the Nile and the Tigris-Euphrates.

No one knows precisely when or where savage men, still millennia away from writing and the other civilized arts, first ventured into the barbarian way of life, when the flint tools of the hunters and gatherers had to be modified into crude hoes and sickles. We are equally hazy about the first domestication of useful animals and birds. There has been much discussion among scholars about which came first, the tamed beast or the planted and tended seed. From it all, one gathers that the two forms of food production replaced the older economy in a series of disjointed and often unrelated steps: that one group might devote itself to domesticating horses or cattle or sheep while another was experimenting with wild wheat or barley; that among peoples who took up both pastoralism and cultivation, the order in which they were adopted varied from group to group; and that for a very long period most societies continued to hunt and fish while they were at the same time trying out one phase or another of food production. In other words, the revolution was no sudden upheaval, but a gradual process extending over many centuries, and in some outlying quarters still continuing. For possibly millennia, those parts of the world in which the great change was taking place must have presented an economic picture not unlike that at the present time, when a variety of economies, each existing in many different stages of development, are in use among mankind.

But it was in the valleys of Egypt and Mesopotamia that the revolution proceeded most rapidly and successfully. There are many reasons why men who have decided to try growing their own food should gravitate to such rivers. It is evident that people who have animals to care for need a dependable supply of drinking water even larger than that required by hunters. Domesticated animals earn their keep, but they must be kept; if men are to profit from the permanent supply of meat, milk, clothing materials, and a host of other products, they must exchange for it a great deal of labor. The beasts must be fed and watered, and the simplest way of satisfying their needs is to pasture them beside a sizable perennial stream. "In Apollonia there is a flock of sheep sacred to the sun; during the daytime these sheep graze along the banks of the river which rises on Mt. Lacmon and after running through Apollonian territory joins the sea by the harbor of Oricus," Herodotus tells us. For thousands of years in the early pastoral period, even after men had learned to dig wells and canals and cattle tanks, this was always the picture: the animals were pastured alongside a river. The larger freedoms men had acquired had already bound them more firmly to the river bank than the reindeer had.

Pasture land, constantly enriched by the droppings of the beasts it feeds, does not readily lose its fertility. Primitive livestock breeders must have noticed this, but it was apparently thousands of years before cultivators thought of collecting manure and applying it to the fields on which they grew crops. Students of the origins of agriculture all seem to agree in the belief that earth's first farmers practiced what is called "hoe culture" or "garden culture." This is the method, still used by extremely primitive peoples in various parts of the world, of burning off a patch of jungle scrub, planting it for one or two seasons, and then, when its fertility is exhausted, moving on to a freshly cleared patch and allowing the former fields to go back to scrub. Letting the exhausted field lie fallow for several years, but keeping it cleared so that it can be easily replanted when it is again ready for use, is a later refinement.

There is only one way in which nature unaided can replace the nutrients taken out of soil by an annual crop. That is by bringing down some large river an annual flood, heavy with silt. The minerals in the silt must be rich in nutrients, and the flood must spread slowly and steadily over low-lying fields and then drain away so gradually that the silt may settle out. The timing is vitally important: ideally, the flood should occur just before the time when seeds must be planted if they are to have a full growing season. Although many rivers flood at some time or other, the classic prototype of such a beneficent inundation is the one that comes down the Blue Nile into the main stream that is formed by its junction with the White Nile. The reason the Blue Nile floods with such monotonous regularity is that it rises in the mountains of Abyssinia; those highlands receive their heavy rains when the southwest monsoon piles up on them the clouds from the South Atlantic Ocean; and that shift of the winds, since it results from the annual tilt of the earth on its axis, recurs with almost mechanical precision. Fortunately, farmers at an early period found the Nile, of all rivers the one with which they could most easily establish a working partnership in the new enterprise of agriculture.

At the time when groups in various parts of the Middle East were making their first experiments with planting, many forces were combining to urge them down to the great rivers where still more daring experiments could be made. Geologists believe that as the ice sheets melted back towards the Arctic regions, and the land to the south of them grew progressively warmer, a shift occurred in the pattern of rainfall from clouds sucked up from the Atlantic Ocean and blown eastward by the prevailing winds. In other words, although there has been no appreciable change in the climate of the Middle Eastern countries and of Africa north of the equator during the last six or eight thousand years, they believe that during the preceding millennia that area suffered a drastic change indeed. Cloud paths shifted north, and rain that had formerly fallen in Africa fell in Europe. As Europe slowly changed from ice field to tundra, and then from steppe to pine forest and finally to well-watered deciduous woodland, so the lands south and east of the Mediterranean changed by imperceptible degrees from well-watered forest and grassland to the desert that is still there.

The theory is that cultivation of plants began in those lands when this long-drawn-out process of desiccation was already well advanced, and savage tribes were tending to gather around fewer and fewer perennial streams as the less vigorous ones dwindled and finally ceased to flow. The dry wadis that at present lead down into the valleys of the Nile and the Tigris-Euphrates must have been still green, though flooded less and less frequently by runoff from rains that were becoming seasonal and finally only occasional. For a long period, small communities who were still hunting but at the same time were beginning to plant did live in such places, as well as along the shores of now vanished lakes, such as the one which then existed in the Fayum depression. The record of their settlements and of their gradual movement into the main valley itself is clearer in Egypt than anywhere else, but it seems logical to suppose that similar transitions went on along the Euphrates, and even by the Indus and the Hwang Ho, though the earliest materials so far unearthed from the valleys of these last two rivers show societies at a much later stage of development, and we have no information about their beginnings.

Food production meant an enormous increase in human security. Having more to eat, and the ability to expand the supply by labor rather than luck, men found themselves stronger both as individuals and as groups. There was much more work to be done, for farming and the care of livestock have never been as easy as hunting, but soon there were more hands to help do it. Whereas children are a burden to the hunter, needing food and care for many years before they are able to draw a bow, the farmer's child can begin at a very tender age to earn his keep by tending flocks, fetching water, and learning to help with weeding, hoeing, harvesting and a dozen other necessary jobs. Whether this is the reason or not, the population did increase noticeably whenever any group made the transition from the feckless economy of taking whatever they could find to the planned labor of food production. Population pressure, demanding that men make fullest use of the new abilities they had acquired, was thus added to the other forces that were impelling men into the great alluvial plains where there were richer opportunities for the cultivator.

When farmers first came down into the valleys of the wide ancient rivers, they entered a landscape totally unlike that whose rich and orderly abundance amazes the modern visitor to Egypt. Seen from the escarpment along its western rim, the valley may have looked as green as it does today, though there was not the sudden break between watered fields and desert. In place of the network of canals guiding the waters out to the farthest fields, there was a vast marshy jungle choked with reeds, above which tall papyri struggled to raise their feathery heads. Here and there in the clotted green mass was the glint of water, as the sunlight picked out for a moment the shifting channels of the river, feeling its sluggish way through the wilderness it had created. There were no boats, for the open stretches belonged to hippopotamuses and crocodiles, as the surrounding swamps belonged to herds of elephant and kudu and wild boar, or to the flocks of waterfowl which nested in the rank growth. Terrible battles were fought in the blind alleys under the reeds; death moved tirelessly through the lotus pads in the service of life; and the silence over the valley, almost as palpable as the mists exhaled by the Nile, muffled the roar as well as the squeal. Through this wild and eerie jungle, the old river moved with the menacing indolence of the crocodile, rousing itself each year to scatter over its flood plain the ashes of dead mountains on which the next year's tender shoots might feed.

For centuries men who needed water for their crops hung about on the hills, looking down into that jungle where the wet greenness never went grey in the drying sun. As the rains came less and less frequently and the dry sands crept closer and closer at their backs, they must have eyed the death-haunted valley with anxiety and greed

59

that increased year by year. For after the exhilarating discovery that men could meddle with nature successfully and to their great profit, there came the first sobering suspicion of the consequence: that once you have begun to interfere with the natural order, you have to keep interfering. They began to notice that their hoe culture was gradually exhausting more and more of the high ground. Yet always there below their settlements was the spectacle of inexhaustible fertility, by some mysterious process endlessly renewed. It was inevitable that sooner or later they must invade the jungle and either subdue it or die.

Since the early cultivators had by no means forgotten how to hunt, probably the first attempts to make clearings on the edges of the flood plain were preceded by countless forays into the depths in search of wild food to supplement their produce. Very likely the first settlers lived by a mixed economy of hunting, fishing, and gathering combined with the cultivation of small cleared patches. Some communities may have reverted to food gathering completely, or the swamps may have been occupied first by people who had refused to give up the old ways and had been pushed out of the more agreeable environments by those who were determined to try the new ones. Certainly, as things worked out, the people who wanted to fish and shoot and trap for a living, who would rather bring down a wild duck on the wing than bother getting food for a tame one, did move progressively deeper and deeper into the wild heart of the marshes. There the stubborn conservatives took up their abode, living the old, wild, precarious life they preferred, while the rest of humanity moved on beyond them towards securities and freedoms they could never hope for and apparently did not want. And there they remain to this day.

Swamps and swamp dwellers have always had a bad

name, largely because the story of human experience has been written by people from other regions. Having chosen an economy in which the civilized arts of communication are inappropriate, and in which they get no chance to arise, the marsh people have lived in the heavy silence of illiteracy. To outsiders their home has been a place of mystery and terror, haunted by nameless evils; the very name of the backwaters they inhabit has become a metaphor for any area of social stagnation where narrow lives and narrower outlooks are bred. Marsh communities are small, and their members are usually isolated from the concerns of the great community of men outside. Because they have achieved such relatively little control over their environment, their freedom of action is severely limited. Thus two of the major drives of humanity—the search for community and the urge towards freedom—tend to disappear. They may use the river as a source of food and drink and for limited transport in a small area. But it is a static relationship, in which men ask nothing of the river beyond what it is freely giving.

To many of the people who first ventured into marsh land, however, cultivating was more attractive than hunting and fishing. In order to follow the preferred way of life, they were obliged to challenge the difficult environment and actively transform it into farm lands. It was a formidable task. It is one thing to clear a patch at the edge of a swamp and drop seeds into the wet mud; but the moment you take land from a river, you have the river to reckon with. And this was an elemental force men had not had to take into account before. If the patch they had cleared happened to lie at exactly the right angle, so that the flood water drained away slowly and evenly, the seeds would sprout and grow without any further care. Nourished by the rich silt, they would produce bountiful harvests. But if the field lay in a very slight depression, the lazy river would leave some of its water to stagnate and the drowned seeds would rot.

To us, looking back after some eight thousand years of agricultural and engineering science, it may seem no great problem; even distinguished archaeologists have been known to remark airily: "All that was needed was for some genius to think of the simple expedient of making channels for the water to flow in." But genius is unfortunately not very common, and what is simple for a child today was once a problem to stagger the most brilliant man alive. The man who first dug a ditch to drain his sodden field and got a good crop for his pains, made a contribution to human life of startling originality and incalculable value.

Where was the surplus water to go? To us it seems obvious that it must flow onto a lower level, and perhaps neolithic men had no difficulty in deciding that it must be sent back into the main river, though to get it there they had to learn a great deal about the relationships of different planes, angles of fall, and other elements of geometry. Somewhere there must have been a low-lying field at the very edge of the flood plain, with a desert strip in a slightly lower depression nearby. And it must have needed another genius to discover it, and to realize that if he drained the extra water on to the dry sand he could do for that outlying bit of desert what the river did for the flood plain.

From these two "simple expedients" have come all the massive drainage and irrigation systems men have since constructed. Those crude ditches in Egyptian or Mesopotamian mud were the ancestors of all canals and all man-made waterways. On the drafting boards of history, they were the first halting, clumsy sketches for California's Imperial Valley. Because they were dug, Vermuyden could drain the English Fens, and Goethals could saw through the mountains of Panama; Jewish refugees can free the ancient plain of Esdraelon from malaria; and coal can travel from a Birmingham warehouse to a London fireplace faster on a barge than in a railway coal car.

Behind all these hopes and triumphs lies the work of barbarian communities who grubbed out their simple ditches in the mud of the cleared swampland. Their achievement was staggering in its implications. Sloshing about knee-deep in the muck of their new fields, with the ancient stench of the swamp soaking into their pores, they hacked away at the bulrush roots with their crude stone mattocks until they had re-established human life on new and more solid foundations. On the hills their ancestors had learned that men might increase the number of edible plants and animals by adding their labor to the efforts of nature. Now they were learning that they could change the face of the earth itself. Between the dry death of the desert and the deadly exuberance of the marsh-jungle, they could create a narrow field for life. And this could happen because they were no longer merely accommodating themselves to the forces of nature; for the first time, they had actually taken hold of the waters that flow over the earth and to a certain limited extent were learning to control them.

In Mesopotamia, different climatic conditions and rivers which do not behave in the same way as the Nile presented problems that had to be solved in somewhat different ways. The Tigris and Euphrates do not flood with the benign regularity of Egypt's river, slowly soaking into the ground enough moisture to last till the harvest; they are apt to burst without warning into roaring masses of water, sweeping everything before them. These destructive floods, which often leave deposits of salt behind them to poison the land, usually come too late for the spring planting season and recede just when they are needed most, as the extreme heat of the rainless summer begins to parch the ground. This heat is much greater than in Egypt; in searing temperatures that sometimes reach 120° F., plants in Mesopotamia must struggle to produce their fruits. The inhabitants of the Twin Rivers valley, therefore, could not develop a system like that of Egypt, based on one annual inundation whose good effects would carry through the growing season. They were obliged to work out methods of perennial irrigation which would bring a steady supply of water to their gardens all through the agricultural year, and at the same time devise ways of minimizing the danger from the tempestuous floods. In other words, they had to learn how to catch at least some of the flood water, and hold it back to be released as needed later on.

The basic engineering structure in such a system is the dam, which must have been, in its earliest form, simply a pile of stones and brushwood across the bed of a wadi. There is some evidence that agriculture in Mesopotamia and Iran began on small alluvial deltas formed by mountain streams as they flowed out onto the plain. It may be that as stream beds became dry wadis, down which water came only occasionally in a sudden heavy spate, people who had formerly used such alluvial deltas thought of the dam as a way of creating a similar environment. In any event, the dam stood out in Mesopotamian thought as the primary invention, the device which had made possible the very creation of the world. The story of that creation which was told and believed for millennia in Sumeria and Babylonia was that the god Ninurta had conquered Kur, the dragon of primeval waters, by building a dam of stones to break the power of the waters and control them so that they could be sent out to irrigate the land. Once a certain measure of flood control was achieved, the construction of canals and ditches to carry the impounded water from

64

the reservoir to the fields would follow as a natural consequence.

The effect of these new departures, both in Egypt and in Mesopotamia, was bound to be felt sooner or later throughout the whole range of human activity. One result was immediate: when a soggy field was drained or a dry one irrigated, the farmer who had done the work was a richer man, more certain where his family's winter meals were coming from. Having invested capital, in the form of his personal hard work, in the land, he began to strike roots in it deeper than were possible on the quickly exhausted patches on the hills. The fanatical devotion of the peasant to his plot of ground was born in human minds. This permanent attachment to the land was possible because he had formed a working partnership with the river, which could be depended upon to bring its yearly gift of moisture and fertilizing silt so long as he kept a firm hand on the reins.

Pushing forward from this newly won vantage, men eventually found themselves living in a society completely different from the one they had brought into the swamps. They moved towards it by a thousand small shifts and detours, throwing aside outmoded tools and habits and ways of thinking, and picking up new ones, until at last they emerged from barbarism into the great riparian cities where civilization could be born. But the transition was long, and slow, and painful. The first triumphant seizure of land from the sweating marshes was followed by a period of consolidation and almost imperceptible change extending over some two thousand years.

There were many reasons why the revolution begun in the muddy ditches and dammed-up wadis could not be completed overnight. For one thing, the drainage and irrigation of a few small but permanently fertile fields gave a family so much food that they had no urgent need of more acres, and the labor of keeping cultivated what they had was a full-time job. The fields could be extended, and very gradually they were, but each advance was more difficult than the previous one. If men moved out into the desert, the life-giving water became more and more reluctant to follow them up the slight incline of the plain; it had to be forced, which meant that men had to ponder and tinker and experiment for centuries to find ways of lifting it to higher levels. Similarly, when the advance was towards the main channel, the point was reached where the water would not drain off a cleared field because there was no lower plane onto which it could flow. Once again, it was necessary to devise some means by which man could lift the unwanted water off his field himself.

But with these lands nearer the main stream there was a further difficulty. The closer they lay to it, the more inclined was the river to flood them daily instead of once a year. To get such fields for their use, men were obliged somehow to head off the waters and push them back, placing between them and the seedbed a barrier of land higher than the plane of the river's surface. In other words, they had to invent another of the basic engineering structures, a variant of the dam across a stream bed. Low ridges of piled-up mud, possibly strengthened by reeds and rushes trampled into their sides, began to arise along the lower edges of the farms, the prototypes of all Dutch dikes and Chinese bunds and English towpaths that protect agriculture today. These long, low embankments could keep the river at bay, but each one had to be higher and stronger than the one farther back: the resistance of the river stiffened with each enforced contraction, much as the pressure in a tire grows with every stroke on a hand pump. Besides that, work on each section of the bund had to be co-ordinated with that on other sections up and down the river. Men began to learn that the solution of one problem can sometimes create others.

This was only one of many new lessons to be mastered if they were to make a success of farming in the reclaimed flood plain. The question of water lifting, as I have said, preoccupied men for generations. When they were still hunters, they had presumably made water-holding vessels from a variety of materials, even including clay. But the needs of a settled agricultural life for grain-storage vessels gave a great impetus to human inventiveness, and soon a rather elaborate assemblage of pots and jars began to gather in their huts. In a clay jar, river water could be held until the silt slowly settled to the bottom, so that men and animals might have a cleaner drink. As droplets seeped through the pores of the coarse clay they would evaporate on the outer surface, giving off the heat that the sun had poured down upon the river and cooling the water in the jar for men's refreshment. In a clay pot, water could be boiled—something that had been extraordinarily difficult when other materials had been used. Water can be heated in a leather bag by dropping hot stones into it, but this method is rather unsatisfactory compared with cooking over a steady fire.

While his wife was using her crude pots for new experiments in making his food more digestible, the farmer was dipping them into an irrigation ditch and laboriously taking up water to pour onto his higher fields. One day he discovered that if he tied a pair of twisted-reed ropes around the neck of the jug, he and his neighbor could swing the jar between them; standing on high ground they could dip, lift, and pour with one long and fairly easy motion, and could thus get both their fields watered with considerably less effort.

Fastening the rope to one end of a long pole laid over a support was another way of making water lifting less strenuous; it is easier for a man to pull down than to lift, and the discovery of the principle of the balance enabled men to take advantage of this fact. With the resulting machine, a downward pull on one end of the pole lifts the bucket of water swinging from the other. But very soon, apparently, someone made a simple but highly useful modification: on the end opposite the bucket, he fastened a heavy blob of clay. This served as a counterpoise, its weight doing much of the work of lifting the filled bucket, and causing the pole to swing easily up and down on its pivot so that the man's labor was reduced to guiding it.

This counterbalanced machine, which is called a *shaduf*, may be another product of the inventiveness of agricultural villagers in the period when they were laying the foundations of irrigation. The earliest representation so far found is on an Akkadian cylinder seal of around 2400–2200 B.C., but the *shaduf* may have been devised much earlier. Because it fits so admirably into a perennial irrigation system, Mesopotamia seems the likeliest place for its invention; in any event it does not appear in Egyptian tomb paintings until around the sixteenth century B.C. But wherever and whenever it originated, the *shaduf* is a landmark in the development of agriculture. Working one of these contrivances, a man can lift and pour an average of six hundred gallons in a day. Since this is so very much more than he could possibly do with any nonmechanical type of water lift, one can imagine that the first users of *shadufs* sang at their work as loudly as their descendants do today in all the Oriental countries where the ancient machine is still in daily use. (PLATE 4)

Since mud was one of the chief natural resources of the river valleys where agriculture was developing, it is not surprising that various kinds of mud should figure in much that men did. The use of clay had developed with great speed from the beginning of the agricultural revolution. At almost all the sites where traces of farming communities have been found, even in the most primitive stage, pottery objects have been associated with the bones and cereal grains and stone implements. Though the ability to make pottery of some sort is no longer regarded as proof that a people had entered on food production, still a variety of earthenware vessels is a sure indication of it. In the river valleys of the Middle East the craft was perfected and elaborated through many stages, from the crude cup patted into shape by the fingers and palm, to the jar built up by coiling a rope of clay round and round, and finally to the beautiful symmetries that can be achieved on a spun wheel. Professor Gordon Childe thinks that the potter's wheel may have been in use in Sumeria as early as the middle of the fourth millennium B.C., and that it reached Syria and Palestine around 3000 B.C., and Egypt some two and a half centuries later. This would indicate that it was another product of the agricultural village economy, though its great development came in the later cities.

It is astonishing how much the human mind did achieve before writing was invented, even with the most unpromising materials it had to work with. Since there were virtually no trees or stones in the former swampland, men had to make do with reeds and mud. From the reeds they learned to make baskets and mats, and even houses. The mud could be tamped down layer on layer to make walls, and when the sun dried it hard, it produced a serviceable framework for a building. Or it could be shaped into rough parallelograms and sun-dried into building bricks, and these could be strengthened by adding a little straw from the harvested fields.

69

Boats were of course a necessity for a riverine people, and here again the reeds were put to service. A bundle of them tied together would float, at least for a time, before it became waterlogged, and would support the weight of a man and his goods. Millennia later, when the great civilizations of Egypt and Mesopotamia had reached their fullest flower and were entering into their long decline, royal barges and swift naval vessels built of fine imported woods still carried in their forms and decorations the traces of those little reed crafts, just as the huge columns at Luxor and the ziggurats of Nineveh preserve the memory of their origins in the dried mud and the bundles of papyrus from the swamps. In Egypt, the reed boat acquired a religious significance, perhaps because it was said that Isis, distracted with grief, had wandered in one through the swamp jungles, seeking the body of Osiris. It came to be believed that the papyrus bundle had the supernatural quality of being unsinkable. Perhaps this is why the magic solar barks of Cheops, recently excavated near the Great Pyramid, conform to the ancient pattern, and carry on bow and stern the carved symbol of the papyrus-reed bundle.

All these fundamental discoveries and inventions were made by people who had almost no tools to work with and nothing but trial and error to guide them. Although they pioneered in so many sciences, they had no scientific tradition to draw on, as we understand the term. In fact, as Henri Frankfort and his colleagues have pointed out, the attitudes and ways of thinking we call scientific were as yet unheard-of. The reeds, the mud, the sunlight, the river were not objects about which men could reason of cause and effect; they were simply other forms of life existing in the world alongside men, with wills of their own and quite unpredictable personalities. To establish any kind of relationship with them a man had to treat them as people, humoring their oddities, appealing to their better nature, and either placating their outbursts of temper or whipping them into submission. As a result, we have the curious example of men doing a fair amount of first-rate scientific work while explaining it as magic, and indeed using magic consciously as the instrument for getting what they wanted.

The Anglo-Saxon beekeeper, living in the same kind of society and in the same frame of mind, spoke to the bees when he wanted them to swarm: "Sit down, spear-women, settle to earth." The Sumerian farmer, feeling a pain in his stomach, ate a little salt; but to make sure it would give him the relief he hoped for, he first made it a speech, flattering it shamelessly, explaining his own name and honorable lineage and the fact that some unknown enemy (whom he had doubtless unwittingly eaten) had bewitched him, and ending up "O Salt, break my enchantment . . . and as my Creator I will extol thee!" Even a thing a man had made with his own hands became a personality in its own right, to be managed with tact and protected against other strong-willed characters who might harm it. Thus a boat needed all kinds of magical assistance: food must be offered to it, and to the river on which its life would be risked, to say nothing of the crocodiles and hippopotamuses who might overturn it if they chose.

The magic associated with boats makes one of the most fascinating and voluminous chapters in the story of primitive thinking, for the same concepts and customs seem to appear wherever men in any early stage of development take to the water. It can be a treacherous bearer, and sometimes the fear of what might happen drove men to take what seem to us horrifying precautions. When a new coracle is launched today at the Kurnool ferry on the

71

Tungabhadra River in India, a sheep is sacrificed and blood is sprinkled over the vessel. On the coast of Madras, they put a pumpkin under the keel to be squashed by the boat as it is pushed into the water, and we are told that the pumpkin is a substitute for the human body which was once offered in the same way. The Solomon Islanders used to place the head of a slaughtered enemy on the prow of a new canoe; and it seems that the moplike decoration of rope or rags still seen on many Mediterranean boats is a relic of similar launching ceremonies in those waters long ago. There is apparently a clear line of descent from the human victim through the animal substitute and the still less offensive pumpkin to the bottle of champagne which is generally sacrificed on such occasions at present.

The use of boats inevitably brought the small agricultural villages into closer contact with one another. The river was a natural highway, connecting the settlements even if they would have preferred to remain isolated. Since they all depended upon it to maintain the way of life they had chosen, they quickly discovered that the needs and aims of one village were very like those of another, and that geography was only one of the forces impelling them to co-operation. At the same time, exchange of ideas and of goods provided a constant stimulation to new adventures and experiments. Men were no longer members only of their particular tribe or settlement; they were also involved in the lives of other peoples following the same occupations in the same valley. When different groups of hunters had lived near the same hunting grounds, the natural limitations of the food supplies had inevitably made them rivals who had to struggle desperately against each other for survival. The farmer's struggle, on the other hand, was with the earth, and he was usually successful enough to produce more than his own family could eat. It was much easier for him and his neighbors to enter into friendly co-operation with other groups of farmers nearby. Slowly, very slowly, the totemic clans that were an inheritance from hunting societies were transformed into what we would call larger political groupings, and the organizations that would finally flower into kingdoms and empires began to evolve.

While men were learning to share work and products with others of their own community, and to find the bases for collaboration with other similar communities, they kept up sporadic contacts with the food-gathering societies that still persisted all around them. Some of these contacts were peaceful, for the hunters would bring them wild game and skins in exchange for the grain of which the farmers now had a constant surplus. But there were also conflicts. Men who have turned a lush, if dangerous, hunting ground into cultivated fields have inevitably trespassed on the interests of those who live by the bow and the trap and the fishline. Removing the source of a man's food is bound to arouse his enmity sooner or later. A cultivated tree is somehow a symbol to the hunter of much that he fears and hates; and these settlers had begun to plant and tend the olive and the date palm. When they were challenged, all the instincts of the peasant were aroused. To them, a tree represented a long-term investment, and the tendency of the gatherer to regard it as a gift of nature was insufferable.

The hunters were fighting a losing battle, and in the final event all they could do was to retreat. A far more persistent challenge came from those who had taken to food production of a different kind. Pastoralism is a kind of halfway stage between hunting and tilling: men control the source of their own food, but they usually depend on nature to fatten it. The herder uses whatever pasture and water he can find, and his life is usually nomadic because he must

73

move his flocks about as the seasons change, bringing fresh grass to different areas. His economic interests are bound to clash with those of the man who must stay beside his fields, jealously guarding the water he has brought to them. The rivalry between Cain and Abel is not easily reconcilable; their story has become the classic example of what may happen when societies built on different economies meet. Times without number in the succeeding centuries they have met at the frontier between the desert and the sown and have fought to the death for control of the water they both need. In Egypt, the advantage lay with the cultivators, probably because the calm beneficence of the Nile favored a regulated, orderly economy such as the farmers were building. The characteristic pattern of development in Mesopotamia, however, where the Tigris and Euphrates are far more wild and unpredictable, is an incursion of nomads into a region made rich by tillage, and the subjection of its people to powerful conquerors who breed livestock for food and hunt lions for pleasure. Continuously since that time nomads have swept out of the Middle Eastern deserts to harry the cultivated lowlands, on occasions threatening to spread their domination far into Europe, Africa, or India.

Before the agricultural revolution, this kind of rivalry between different economies had not existed. Food production brought into being for the first time different ways of making a living, and planted the seeds of conflicting interest whose fruits have not yet been finally gathered.

It also planted deep in men's minds the idea of property, of a right to possession even of the common earth. For the fields on reclaimed swampland were not the gifts of nature, who gives to all her creatures equally and with no sign of favoritism or even justice. They had been won by human labor, and it seemed right that a man who had dug a ditch should have first claim on the water flowing through it. The river of course did part of the work, so much that without it men would have worked in vain, but it was really the man who had brought forth the land by forcing the river to assist him.

When property rights were threatened by outsiders, the villagers naturally called on neighboring villages to make a common defense. This kind of collaboration—and it must have been frequent—drew them still more closely into a larger community. Millennia later, you can see Athenians, who had looked with a certain disdain on Spartans or Thebans, beginning, in a time of similar common danger, to talk of themselves, and of any "foreigners" they could persuade into an alliance, as Greeks. It is a familiar pattern of human behavior, and it added its weight to the other forces that were impelling men into organized states.

These forces were legion. The need for better drinking water than came out of irrigation ditches, for example, had led men to dig wells through which they could tap waters that had been filtered through the sand. But a good well can supply a whole village, and it was natural that the digging of it should become a community undertaking. Such communal labor naturally conferred communal rights of property in the water, and gave the group the right to dole it out to individuals on terms decided by the group. This gave a very powerful impetus to the growth of the new and larger social organization, for the ability to withhold water could be used to force any rugged individualist into obedience to the new authority. Larger drainage and irrigation works, undertaken by the whole community, or by several villages together, also produced new wealth that must be shared by all who had helped, and they strengthened the authority of the larger group in the same way. It did not take men long to realize that

75

they could sometimes surrender a minor freedom to the community in exchange for a major one.

Finally, the growing complexity of society resulted in an entirely new kind of community, which began to appear late in the preliterate period. A town is not merely larger than the earlier agricultural village; it is different in kind, because different things are done in it. The new inventions that had made it possible for farmers to produce more than their families could consume had also made self-sufficiency impossible. A man simply could not be expert at all the new tasks that had to be done if he wanted good harvests, and even if he could, he had not the time to make boats, build *shadufs,* turn a potter's wheel, learn simple engineering, and perform the necessary magic all these activities required. Some jobs could be given over to children or to women or even to animals, and for others he could combine forces with his neighbors. But there came a time when it seemed more sensible to give some of his surplus grain to a man who was cleverer than he at making the things a farmer needs to work with. Towns were the places where these new craftsmen lived; they were the homes of the first people in the world who could get food without either seizing it personally from nature or producing it out of the ground by the sweat of their brows.

Once the towns were peopled, society was again on the verge of dramatic change. New economic forces were set in motion, and as they began to be felt the farming that had brought them into being prepared to transfer to them its dominance over the affairs of men. It is true that the farming life was richer and safer and altogether more satisfying than the old hunting life, but it still gave little scope for all kinds of creative abilities some men were beginning to realize they possessed. It could not satisfy the desires of those who did not want to be tied to the soil, nor the cravings of some for a wider and more diversified community than the village where all did the same work and talked about the same subjects. The final achievement of neolithic barbarism was its creation of forms of social organization men could use to free themselves of its limitations.

Before the appearance of towns, however, in which civilization could be invented, the farming villagers had perfected many tools that would be used in that invention. And it is hard to escape the conclusion that the principal stimulator of their activity was the river along whose banks they had made their fields. Rivers had certainly called forth their engineering; it is now becoming clear that rivers also prompted some of their purely intellectual endeavors. For example, it used to be thought that the calendar, the device that made time comprehensible and measurable, and history possible, resulted from astronomical observations. This opinion arose from the fact that the Dog Star (Sirius) makes its annual reappearance on the horizon at dawn just about the time the Nile flood normally reaches Cairo, and it was thought that the early farmers learned to predict this most vital event in the agricultural year by looking out for the star. Everybody agreed that farmers had discovered the solar year; they could not use the lunar phases that had sufficed for the hunter because planting and harvesting must go in yearly cycles, not in four-weekly ones. But recently it has been suggested that the star seems an unlikely source for their great discovery; more probably, they found that a year has 365 days by simply observing the Nile, since it was the most obvious thing in sight and its movements dominated their whole life. They kept track of the flood itself, noting the number of days between successive appearances of this climactic event and averaging them out over a period of, say, fifty years. Because this

77

method would produce a slight inaccuracy, which would increase into a noticeable error over a period of centuries, later priests and magicians would use astronomical observations in order to predict the arrival of the flood more accurately, and possibly even to bolster a claim that they could themselves cause it. If this is the way things were, then it was men's study of the river's ways, and not their stargazing, that enabled them to begin to keep a record of their affairs. Specialists in these matters have worked out the date when the calendar must have been initiated; most of them choose the year 4236 B.C. as the first date, the beginning of *recorded* time. It is perhaps ironic that this should be so very near the mythical date for the Creation of the world, which Bishop Usher arrived at by working backwards through the legendary genealogies in the Bible.

In a sense, of course, the creation of much of our world as we know it does date from the period when men in the deltas of the Nile and the Twin Rivers were separating the land from the waters, bringing the order of settled agriculture out of marshy chaos, and planting what must have seemed to them a paradise. In later periods, when men had taken on the burdens of civilization along with its amenities, they looked back to these early times as to a golden age. We today would hardly describe it in those terms, but we do recognize that though there must have been many ups and downs through the long centuries of barbarism, many setbacks and failures, there is a fairly clear line of what we must call progress.

In a way, the calendar indicates the end of an age; it is a culminating event in a process of social consolidation and growth that could not go much farther without transforming the society that had produced it. Indeed, by the time the calendar was instituted, the transformation was already well under way. The farmers had led humanity to

78

the threshold of civilization, but like Moses they could not lead on into the promised land. That was a job for the townsmen, who owed their very existence to the inventiveness and productivity of the men who had drained the marshes with their own hands. The cultivators had played their great revolutionary role; from this point onward their labor would be the foundation on which all human achievement must ultimately rest, but it could never again be, as it once was, the crowning pinnacle. Farming, like hunting before it, has become the refuge of conservatism. True, it has been transformed time after time by new inventions and devices, until today it is, in the advanced countries, a craft demanding the highest skill in a dozen sciences and arts. There is nothing "backward" or arrested about contemporary agriculture. There are still societies in the world where the introduction of even a few of its modern techniques can bring revolutionary improvements in human living. But as a force of creative change, able to alter the whole direction of human progress, its work was done in the rich ferment of barbarian society when for its sake men dared to take hold of the rivers with their hands and say to their waters, "Flow here!"

CHAPTER IV

Kings, Traders, and Soldiers

FROM some points of view, the rise of the first cities is another of those epochal events which transform the whole of human society, altering established patterns of behavior and setting up new goals. So much happened in the new cities that began to grow up along the Nile, the Tigris-Euphrates, and the Indus five or six thousand years ago, the townsmen embarked on so many new adventures of the mind, and did it so suddenly, that scholars now describe the period in Professor Childe's phrase, "the urban revolution." They mean by this that the gathering of men into cities is comparable with the domestication of plants and animals or with the widespread use of machinery as a landmark of human progress.

It is astonishing how quickly the fertility of the city as a breeding ground for new ideas and techniques began to be evident. As long as every man had been obliged to spend the major part of his time and effort in working directly on the land, all his potential talents for other kinds of labor had lain more or less idle. It was the driving necessity to hunt day and night for food that had kept humanity trapped for hundreds of thousands of years within the limitations of a savage economy; individual genius for other activities had had no opportunity to exercise itself, and even the great art of the Magdalenian culture had been possible only because it served to bring success in the hunt. In the same way, tillage and pasturage had been full-time occupations for the entire community for some two thousand years after their discovery. It was only when long practice had enabled a farmer to produce much more food than he and his own family could consume that the man whose talents were for other kinds of work could leave off farming, move into one of the new cities, and begin to follow his particular bent. Civilization—by which we mean social organization, literature, religion, trade, the elaboration of arts and sciences—could arise only through the collective efforts of a multitude, each doing the labor he liked best and for which he was best fitted. Once this state of affairs was reached, humanity was catapulted forward into a period of enormous creative activity. Within a relatively short period, men in the new urban centers organized themselves into powerful city-states and kingdoms, perfected elaborate systems of religion and laws, discovered the use of metals, invented public architecture and developed it to staggering proportions, built up networks of trade that were to persist for millennia, and by the invention of writing forged the most effective instrument for still further advance.

In this initial release of the human spirit, and in the swift evolution that followed it, from city-state to kingdom to the vast empires of the ancient world, the rivers flowing past city walls or market places played a role of considerable importance. Historians of these early ages see in river control, indeed, the mainspring that actually set off the urban revolution, for it was only through drainage and irrigation that food production was increased enough to support the classes who could create cities and, with them, civilization. But the influence of the river in human affairs did not stop there. The relationship between men and the great bodies of moving water on whose banks they built their first cities provides a thread along which we can trace something of the whole experience of societies moving from a cluster of mud huts along the Tigris to the grandeur of that marble city whose broken aqueducts and ruined cisterns the Tiber still reflects. It is not the only thread in the tapestry of ancient civilization, of course, nor perhaps even the principal one. Neither is it distinguished by many technological innovations. With one or two possible exceptions, we shall not find that men in the period between, say, 3500 B.C. and the rise of the classical empires were able to establish any totally new and unprecedented relationship with the rivers of the earth—nothing comparable in its revolutionary impact with such a discovery as fishing.

What we do find is an extraordinary proliferation from seeds planted by paleolithic and neolithic men, a host of remarkable developments in which men perfected and elaborated ideas inherited from their predecessors. Qualitatively, in the absolute sense, there may be little change in the relationship with rivers until men come near the end of the ancient imperial age and are preparing to transform society again into the modern world we still inhabit, but the quantitative changes are enormous. The mud ditches grow into wide canals on which ocean-going vessels can sail from the Nile to the Red Sea; they expand into a network of inland waterways on which barges loaded in Britain can move across Europe to bring tribute to Marseilles and thence to Rome. Flowing water is lifted up on the back of aqueducts striding down the hills to Nineveh or Segovia, that city dwellers in the hot plains may drink from distant mountain streams. The pile of sticks and stones across a gully at the edge of the Mesopotamian plain is transformed into the huge masonry dam that creates Lake Homs in the desert of Syria, or the Marib dam whose impounded waters nourished a civilization for many centuries in the desert hills of southern Arabia. Up and down the rivers the trade routes lengthen to suck the wealth of unknown lands into the urban vortex. The river becomes a boundary between warring empires, its fording places a battlefield into which men are driven by whips to struggle in the currents under the weight of their clumsy shields. The limits of knowledge expand, and as men become conscious of those limits they begin to wonder about what may lie beyond; as they attempt to define the unknown, it is the known river that they seize upon as a living symbol for their dreams and fears and speculations. The eternal mysteries of sleep and birth and death are figured in their minds as dark and silent streams, and the map of their small actual world ends at the fabled circling flood of the River Oceanus.

The river, in short, was the requisite without which the early civilizations could never have arisen, and for millennia it remained a central fact in their existence. The need for a permanent water supply made the river bank the natural site for a city, just as it had been for a paleolithic settlement, but the water meant far more to townsmen than it could ever mean to hunting folk. The basic necessity for drinking water was the same, though the quantity demanded by a city was far greater. But for civilized men this was only the simplest service the river performed. Lifted out of the stream by *shadufs* and flowing through cunningly directed channels, it came into their homes to bring coolness and refreshment, to bathe their bodies and wash their garments, and to create a green shade in their courtyards. The intense heat of the Mesopotamian sun was mitigated by river water trickling down reed screens, in a curious anticipation of modern air conditioning. Pavements and streets were cleansed with it, and it was an indispensable tool in most of the industrial processes that furnished the equipment for civilized living. All things made of clay, from the walls of their houses to the pots and pans in their kitchens, owed something of their existence to the river. So did their textiles, which could not be extracted and manufactured without the aid of water. In Mesopotamia, the tablets on which merchants kept their accounts and poets recorded their epics were things of clay, and later on, a material on which one could write with ink was made by a process that required quantities of water for soaking the papyrus. When men of Sumer drank beer, or poured libations to their gods, they owed these refinements of living to their river, just as their wives did when they sat at their dressing tables painting their lips and adjusting golden pins in their hair. Even regarded purely as the source of drinking water, a sizable perennial river was an absolute prerequisite for the existence of an ancient city.

This is one of the reasons, though only one, why the ancient cities stood where they did. If you go today to Damascus, possibly the oldest continuously inhabited city in the world, as you come down the steep road from the heights of the Anti-Lebanon you will get a vivid impression of the meaning of rivers to men back in the dawn of urban life. The mountains themselves are almost bare, dusty and dry and heavily eroded, and as you come over the topmost ridge you see ahead to the east the utter blankness of the Syrian desert, leveling out endlessly towards Iraq, on and on without a visible signpost or a tree, in a landscape that seems empty of human beings or of any other creatures. The road keeps dropping down, twisting over rocky humps and into desolate gullies, and you feel you are entering a land where life has never breathed and never can. Then, quite suddenly, it swings round a spur of the foothills, and your eyes are momentarily blinded by a gush and swirl of intense greenness, surging out of the bare rock and pouring into a great pool of acacia and palm branches. One who has not seen an oasis in a desert cannot understand what emotions the green banner of Islam stirs in the souls of its followers. Damascus stands like such a banner, flaunting in the face of the desert the triumphant assertion of what men can do with a river, the green of its gardens starred with glistening domes and towers, and the air above it shaken with the busy sounds of human life.

It is sometimes said that Damascus is the creation of the Barada River, which comes suddenly out of the mountains to water its small valley, but this is no more true than to say that Egypt is the creation of the Nile. They both owe their existence to man's use of the river, his assertion of at least partial control over its waters, and his ingenuity in devising ways to make it serve his purposes. It is not nature alone nor man alone that has made us, but the relationships we have willed and established. The elaborate plumbing facilities of Mohenjo-Daro and Harappa forty-five hundred years ago were fed by the Indus, but they were conceived and built by the people who used them. The stream called Elisha's well did not make Jericho, but without it men could not have built the walls that fell before Joshua's trumpets, nor can they live there today unless their women go to it daily to fill their jugs and walk home with the burden on their heads, more stately than queens under the weight of crowns.

Small cities could subsist on meager streams. Agamemnon's Greeks, in his capital of Mycenae, drank from the spring Perseia; in the thirteenth century B.C. they cut an amazing tunnel down through the Cyclopean ramparts and the solid rock beneath so that if in time of siege the defenders of the city should be driven up into the citadel they could still reach the water on which their survival depended even more than upon their arms. When the empires spread so wide that caravan routes had to cross vast desert spaces, the citizens of a small trading post like Nabataean Petra, chiseled out of the sandstone in a gorge of the Moabite hills, could become absolute arbiters of trade because they had channeled the tiny stream from Ain Musa, Moses' spring, through their rocky streets.

Byblos was another relatively small town, but its site near the River of Adonis made it vastly important. As Damascus is the longest-persisting great city, so Byblos is the oldest town that still lives, so far as we know. It has always been a focal point on the Levant coast line, drawing pilgrims and soldiers and traders to its harbor near the mouth of the Adonis. At the time of the winter floods, the river brings down such quantities of red silt from the iron-bearing strata it cuts through in the mountains that men said it flowed with the blood of the dying god, and stood in awe on its banks to watch it discolor the sea in a great deltaic stain spreading out several miles from the shore. Drops of the divine blood splashed out onto the land, and wherever one fell the scarlet anemone, Adonis' flower, sprang into bloom. In the intervals between these annual religious phenomena, Byblos lived on traffic, taking the logs of fir and cedar that were floated down the stream and lashing them together into rafts in the calm water of the harbor, ready to be towed across the Mediterranean to Egypt or to the western lands.

With any of the great cities, the presence of a river at its side was even more vital, and such obligations were laid on it that only one of the largest streams would suffice. That is why, before engineering had developed to the point where gigantic canals and aqueducts and well systems could be constructed, Memphis and Thebes had to be on the Nile, as Babylon and Nineveh on the Euphrates and Tigris, and Mohenjo-Daro on the Indus. The growth of Susa, the capital from which the Persians under Cyrus overran the world, was limited by the smaller flow of its river Choaspes, as was Jerusalem's by the scattered springs in the dry Judean hills. And it was only after men had mastered a thousand tricks of hydraulics that a caravan stop like Palmyra, midway in the desert between the Barada and the Euphrates, could be built at all.

The earliest cities have long since died and completely disappeared, so that today we cannot see them as they once were. Despite the epoch-making work of archaeologists like Sir Leonard Woolley, we cannot quite picture Ur of the Chaldees as it must have looked five thousand years ago, towering up above its foundations in the Euphratean mud at the point where at that time the river entered the Persian Gulf. But in the fifth century B.C., Herodotus visited Babylon, and he has left us a description of that fabulous city as he saw it, already a capital of great antiquity and hastening towards its final obliteration, but still retaining the outward form it had shown to so many generations. From his notes we get a fairly clear picture of the look of an ancient riverine capital.

Babylon lies in a wide plain, a vast city in the form of a square with sides nearly fourteen miles long and a circuit of some fifty-six miles, and in addition to its enormous size it surpasses in splendor any city of the known world. It is surrounded by a broad deep moat full of water, and within the moat is a wall fifty royal cubits wide and two hundred high. . . . The Euphrates, a broad, deep, swift river which rises in Armenia and flows into the Persian Gulf, runs through the middle of the city and divides it in two. The wall is brought right down to the water on both sides, and at an angle to it there is another wall on each bank, built of bricks without mortar, running through the town. There are a great many houses of three and four stories. The main streets and the side streets which lead to the river are all dead straight, and for every one of the side streets or alleys there is a bronze gate in the river wall by which the water could be reached. (Herodotus, Bk. I, pp. 84–85. This and all later references to Herodotus are by book and page number in *The Histories*, tr. Aubrey de Selincourt, Penguin, 1954.)

The straightness of the streets immediately suggests an orderliness, a sense of highly organized civic life, which may run counter to our previous impressions of early Oriental cities. Yet in the large urban centers of the five-thousand-year-old civilization recently excavated along the Indus River, there is a grid plan as regular as anything Romans or Americans ever built. Such exactness in town planning may not have been characteristic of all the earliest cities, but it may at least be taken as a symbol of the social organization which the cities quickly evolved.

The concentration of large numbers of people, each pursuing his own economic goal and constantly encroaching on the privileges of others, necessitated some kind of centralized authority which all must agree to obey. Fair trade practices had to be established, the water supply had to be controlled and shared, the surrounding countryside on which the city depended for its food had to be extensively irrigated, and the defenses of the city organized. To fill this need, "kingship descended from on high," as the Sumerian chroniclers put it.

Whether kingly authority was an early and spontaneous invention, or whether it evolved slowly and gradually out of a council of citizens delegating their power occasionally at first, but with increasing frequency until they finally surrendered it completely, is a question that need not detain us. What is significant is that the need for a final authority, a supreme governing power, was normally met in the earliest city-states by concentrating it in the person of one man, the king. From this point onward for millennia, the record of human experience is to be found in the accounts of what kings did, or what was done in their names. The king is the personification of organized urban society, and through his activities we can see many of the impulses and aims of the citizenry.

At the heart of that society lay the river, and the primary function of the king, as administrator and symbolic head of the state, was to watch over its use and control. The Chinese people have always classified their rulers as "good dynasty" or "bad dynasty," according to whether they kept up the waterworks or let them fall into disrepair. It is evident that people in the early Middle Eastern kingdoms judged their rulers by similar standards, for whenever a king wished to boast to posterity of his good deeds he put high on his list of accomplishments some such brag as that of Amenemhet I, who flourished around 2000 B.C.: "I grew corn, I loved Neper the grain god; in every valley the Nile greeted me; none hungered, none thirsted during my reign." The Lords of Lagash, a small city-state in Sume-

89

ria about the same time, made similar boasts about their prowess in digging canals and building dikes. And centuries later Queen Semiramis of Assyria still thought it necessary to inscribe on her tomb: "I constrained the mighty river to flow according to my will and led its waters to fertilize lands that had before been barren and without inhabitants."

Such activity was demanded of those who ruled. One of the earliest representations we have of any Egyptian monarch shows a king called Scorpion performing what he and his people must have regarded as his most important public function: in a ceremony far more necessary than the usual laying of a cornerstone, he is opening the dike so that the fields may receive the annual flood. This ancient ceremonial turning of the first spadeful was still performed as late as the nineteenth century, on the annual "day of breaking the river." (PLATE 5)

The king's function as guardian of the river was not confined to ceremony, but was a never-ending workaday job, upon whose satisfactory performance hung the welfare of the state. By the time the cities arose, the Nile valley and delta had been largely cleared of swamp, and the land divided up into holdings of 1,000 to 40,000 acres, each enclosed by dikes and crisscrossed with smaller ridges separating the fields. Out from the river the main irrigation canals ran between these big estates, branching into a maze of smaller and smaller channels to the farthest clearings. The dikes needed constant repair, especially the big ones that confined the old river to its main channel, and an elaborate system of accounting and management was necessary to see that the waters were fed out fairly to all, and that no man trespassed on another's rights and property. That the same needs were present in Mesopotamia is shown by the provision in Hammurabi's Code (c. 1750

B.C.): "If anyone opens his canals to let in water, but is careless and the water floods the field of his neighbor, he shall measure out grain to the latter in proportion to the yield of the neighboring field." Much of the work of the central government was delegated to lesser authorities, and already in the Egyptian Old Kingdom (roughly twenty-seventh to twenty-second centuries B.C.) there were district governors. It is significant that the first in their list of titles was "Digger of Canals," for with them, as with the king himself, the first obligation of office was the up-keep of the irrigation system in their area and the organization of the countryside to meet any emergency that might threaten it.

There were such emergencies, of course. Even the Nile is not mechanically perfect, and there were times when it failed to bring down its normal quantity of water. When this happened, the "Diggers of Canals" mobilized their forces, under orders from the capital, and enforced the laws on distribution of what water there was. Occasionally the reverse happened, and the Nile came down in such a flood that it overwhelmed the embankments and swept away men's houses and cattle, destroying all hope of a harvest the following year. At such times every able-bodied man was called to the dikes, and the scene was much like that on the Mississippi today when an unusually large flood pours down to the Gulf of Mexico. One such flood in 683 B.C. turned the whole Nile Valley into "a primordial ocean, an inert expanse"; it was the result of completely unprecedented rainfall in Nubia, so that a White Nile flood was added to the usual one from the Blue, to the great joy of the King of Nubia, who has recorded the woes of wealthy Egypt in a gleeful inscription because his own people, for once, gathered an abundant harvest. In such a flood, boundary markers were apt to be swept away, and

91

not the least important duty of the royal agents was to resurvey the land and establish property rights as they had been.

Normally, the Egyptians were able to handle any but the widest variations in the flood level, because they had worked out a fine system of measurement and communication. The famous Nilometer was simply a series of high-water and low-water marks placed on prominent buildings or cliffs at many points in the valley, all the way up to the first cataract. As the time of the great flood drew near, the height of the Nile was anxiously watched, and checked against the readings of previous years, and from the uppermost of these gauge stations swift rowers were sent downstream one after another to report the latest readings to the authorities in the capital. Rowing hard with the current, they were able to outrace the flood so far that by the time it reached the populous centers the inhabitants were prepared for it.

It is not in the occasional catastrophes, however, but in the normal day-to-day activity of the kings that we see how central was the role of the river. The chief story told of Menes, a legendary character who, tradition said, had first united delta and upper valley into one kingdom, was that he had placed a great dam across the Nile in order to divert the river around the site of his capital, Memphis. The story is apocryphal, but there was certainly a dam there when Herodotus visited Memphis, and it may have replaced an earlier one. In any event, the art of building a large dam had been mastered at a very early date. Possibly the oldest dam of which any trace remains today is the one that was built across the Wadi Gerrawi more than two thousand years before the Christian era. There, on the eastern desert rim of Egypt, a small colony of workmen quarried alabaster for the temples and pyramids in the valley, and to assure their water supply a rough masonry dam was thrown up, 270 feet thick and 370 feet long, to impound the occasional flash floods that swept down the gully. It is faced with limestone on the water side, and the ruins that still stand give clear evidence that the art of dam building had already reached a very high state of perfection. It is possible that the stone dike which creates Lake Homs by damming the Orontes in Syria was the work of Egyptian invaders; it is still in use, its walls often repaired and extended but with the original stones still in place. According to Julian Huxley, the lake is "reputed to be the earliest large artificial reservoir in the world." All the Mesopotamian rulers were familiar with dams and expert in their construction; like the Egyptians, in their imperial periods they spread their engineering skill far and wide, so that even the Marib dam in Arabia is thought by some to have been inspired by the Assyrians after their conquest of the peninsula in the seventh century B.C.

Nothing seems to have stopped the early kings when they set out to supply water to the cities they ruled and the farm lands that fed them. An Assyrian inscription of around 1240 B.C. tells how the city of Nimrud was supplied by a royal canal, "cutting through the low-lying places according to the cord [i.e., in a straight line] and carrying it through the difficult places of the high mountains through tunnels of rock." Its builders had a long tradition of such works behind them. Centuries before the various warring city-states in Mesopotamia were united under the control of Babylon, a series of great waterways had connected the Tigris with the Euphrates where they ran roughly parallel through their lower courses; and each of the cities in Sumer and Akkad had been surrounded in the third millennium B.C. with its own network of canals radiating from it to the limits of its dominion. The maintenance of these canals, the control of traffic on them and the collection of tolls, the strict administration of everything to do with drainage, irrigation, and water supply, was the daily concern of the kings. The whole system of law, for which they were principally responsible, grew up from their decisions, and a surprising number of the regulations in such a body of rules as Hammurabi's Code deal directly with water. Ordinary official documents and letters show equally plainly the overriding concern: "Summon the people who live on this side of the Damanu canal, that they may scour it."

In Egypt, water problems were a constant preoccupation of the Pharaohs. As their rule was extended beyond the area where the Nile could supply all their needs, they were forced to seek for other sources of water. Sometimes, as in the Wadi Gerrawi, they dammed an intermittent stream; more often, they dug wells. In doing so, they were not inventing, but perfecting a device already ancient. The earliest dug wells which have been discovered, in the Indus Valley, are conjecturally dated around 3000 B.C.; but since savages and even animals have been observed to make hollows in dry stream beds and drink the water that seeps into them, the idea of a well seems to date back to the dawning of consciousness. Before actual writing was invented, the earliest pictographs from the sites of the first Sumerian cities include a circular mark which is translated as "well" or "cistern." But like many other techniques inherited from older societies, well digging was perfected by the urban communities and elaborated with great skill. An Egyptian officer who was sent to the Red Sea coast on an expedition around 2000 B.C. reported back that he had dug fifteen wells to supply the workers in quarries along the route. He also remarks, "I gave to each a leather bottle and a carrying pole and two jars of water and twenty loaves daily."

As the passion for massive architecture became a mania with the Pharaohs, quarries were of increasing importance, and since the stone was always to be found outside the valley, in the dry and barren hills, the problem of water supply for the quarrymen was never-ending. We owe the pyramids and temples and the monumental sculpture to its successful solution. The river itself was forced into use in the work of building, not only when huge slabs of stone from the Arabian hills were ferried across it, or when it carried heavily loaded rafts down from the granite quarries of Aswan, but as an actual tool. Herodotus, when he was shown a large artificial lake near the Nile, was at first puzzled as to what had been done with the mountains of earth that must have been excavated. Then he remembered a tale he had been told in Assyria, of how some thieves had got into Sardanapalus' underground treasure house at Nineveh by digging a tunnel into it; they were able to work in secret because "every night they dumped the soil they took out into the Tigris, which flows past the city." So it was with the Egyptian excavators: "they dug it out and flung it into the Nile, and knew well enough that the Nile would carry it away and get rid of it."

As engineering skill increased, men were constantly building, and constantly tampering with the rivers that flowed by their cities. In the earlier Babylonian kingdoms, the Euphrates flowed through the middle of the capital in a natural channel, whose mud banks must have made a great deal of trouble for the inhabitants by caving in and by being always slippery. Perhaps the reason the banks were not strengthened and lined was that men could not figure out how to work with stone or brick under water. But when the vigorous rulers of the so-called Neo-Babylonian period (c. 612–539 B.C.) were making their city the wonder of the world, they found an opportunity to do the needed work. As part of an elaborate system of water defenses upstream from the capital, they made a large artificial lake by deepening a natural depression and diverting the river into it. The bed through the city naturally dried up while this diversion was going on, and workmen were able to build solid brick embankments along both sides before the basin was filled and the Euphrates flowed back into its accustomed channel.

Apparently at the same time, Babylon acquired its first bridge. Herodotus describes it as a series of stone piers connected by "squared baulks of timber laid down for the inhabitants to cross by—but only during daylight, for every night the timber was removed to prevent people from going over in the dark and robbing each other." Probably the people were not so thievish as Herodotus suggests, however, for Diodorus Siculus says that the two halves of the city were also connected by a tunnel under the river, fifteen feet wide and twelve feet high, lined with bricks and coated with bitumen to make it watertight. It would appear, therefore, that twenty-five hundred years ago men and donkeys and camels could walk dry-shod under the Euphrates as easily as automobiles and trucks today speed under the Hudson or the Maas or the Thames.

For the trade that was one of the primary characteristics of urban life, the construction of wharves and jetties was as necessary as bridge building or laws to control the movement of boats and rafts. All early trade centered on the rivers, which were highways long before roads were thought of. It is no accident that the towns which became great urban centers in the ancient world were all on the lower reaches of rivers, for they were essentially consumers and they became great because the traffic could flow easily down to them bringing the tribute of the hills. The very earliest towns, of course, had grown up on reclaimed swampland near the mouths of the rivers. But the great capitals of antiquity—Babylon, Memphis, Nineveh, Mohenjo-Daro—were a little farther upstream where they could command the wide plain, controlling not only the low-lying farm lands and the approaches from the sea but, even more importantly, the upper reaches of their river and its principal tributaries, since it was down these streams that most of their essential raw products came.

Primitive conditions of land transport made the rivers almost the only means of moving heavy loads. Not until the time of the Assyrian empire was there any organized road building, and their highway system never rivaled the splendid one constructed later by the Incas in South America. Even if there had been good roads in ancient Egypt and Mesopotamia, heavy traffic could hardly have moved on them. Oxen are incredibly slow, and men did not know how to harness them in tandem so that many animals could combine their power to pull one load. Horses, donkeys, and onagers could not pull heavy loads because the ox harness, which they were obliged to wear, choked them if they strained against it. Also, they had no proper horseshoes; not until the fourth century B.C. were animals shod, and then only with clumsy soles of leather or straw or metal which were temporarily tied on their feet when they came to a rough or slippery place. Neither the horse collar nor the true iron horseshoe, permanently attached, was known in the centers of civilization until the early Middle Ages, when Europeans adopted them from nomadic tribes who had in turn borrowed them from the horsemen of the Central Asian steppes. Lacking these two inventions, there was only one way by which heavy cargo could be moved quickly and at a reasonable cost, and that was on rafts floating down a river.

But it could hardly move upstream at all: rowed boats could make little progress against the swift currents of the Tigris and Euphrates, and for loaded poled rafts the journey was impossible. On the Nile, when the papyrus swamps were disappearing before advancing agriculture and boats began to be built of imported wooden planks, less effort was needed to row against the sluggish flow, but even there a journey upstream in a rowed craft was a slow and strenuous business. The Nile, however, is almost unique among river valleys in having a strong prevailing upstream wind, which blows steadily from the sea all the year round, except for the brief period when the *khamseen* comes like an oven blast from the Sahara. Once sails were invented, large and heavily laden craft could make good headway up the Nile, a fact that may have had much to do with making Egypt a maritime power. The downstream situation of the Mesopotamian capitals likewise explains much of their importance as centers of trade.

It also accounts for the kind of boats that traveled down to them. Herodotus says that in his time the Euphrates swarmed with round coracles, boats made of skin stretched over a framework of withies, each carrying a donkey among the piles of cargo so that when the city was reached the boat could be dismantled and carried back upriver by land. His only mistake, according to Hornell, is that when his Babylonian hosts told him about enormous craft that came down the river at the season of high water (when Herodotus was not there) he supposed they meant coracles like the ones he saw, only far bigger. Hornell makes it clear that the big vessels, able to carry more than a hundred tons of wine in palmwood casks, were actually log rafts buoyed up by hundreds of skin floats, for, as he says, a round boat large enough for the job could not negotiate the rapids nor be manageable even in the calmer stretches. It was on these rafts, apparently, that producers of wine in Armenia, of timber in the Amanus range, or of copper in the Kurdish hills brought their goods to market. When the shipment was sold, and they had made their necessary purchases of portable articles from the bazaars, they could pack up the deflated skins and take them home by donkey-back for use the following year, while the logs could be sold for a fancy price to the city dwellers.

Trade established up and down a particular river valley was a powerful unifying force; it was one phase of the river's central role in establishing cohesive kingdoms out of the disparate city-states. But it worked just as effectively for expansion into still larger kingdoms and empires. As the demand for imported products grew, caravan routes began to be connected by a kind of portage service from one river system to another. This brought new and exotic merchandise into the market place, and as these products gradually came to be regarded as necessities, they created their own demand. To satisfy it, merchants went farther and farther afield, following previously unknown rivers up to mines and distant farm lands in quest of precious stones, rare metals, and plants that yielded all manner of strange fruits, spices, and perfumes with which they might tempt sophisticated shoppers in the cities. It was this desire to draw on wider and wider sources that led Sargon the Akkadian, in the period around 2350 B.C., to extend his dominions "to the silver mountains and the cedar forest" (by which he probably means the Taurus and Amanus ranges), thus creating the first genuine empire. It did not persist for long, but it furnished the pattern for all the sprawling tribute-collecting governments that were to follow, the pattern, indeed, that was to characterize human life in all the advanced civilizations from the rise of the Persians right down to the fall of Rome.

This kind of expansion naturally meant war, for there is a limit beyond which barbarian producers cannot be persuaded to part with their goods peaceably, and the limit is too low to yield what the average adventurer considers a good profit. Wars among the earliest city-states seem to have arisen principally out of conflicts over water rights and irrigation systems, but the kingdoms, and even more the empires, fought principally for control of raw materials. Under the pressure of their constant campaigns, military science, and specifically military engineering, reached astonishing heights. And always foremost in the thinking of the commanders, in the planning of all their tactics and strategy and logistics, was the river, raising its provocative questions: how it could be used as a shield, or as a weapon; how it could be crossed by hordes of men with their pack animals, their wagons and chariots, and their cumbersome baggage; how it could be made to furnish drink for the mercenaries under their whips.

For many of the citadels, a river provided some sort of natural shield. It was hard to attack and easy to defend, and fortunate was any town that stood in the bend of a stream where the water could almost encircle its walls. Those not so happily situated often tried to create artificial water barriers. Nebuchadnezzar, when he dug the great reservoir above Babylon, made at the same time an elaborate series of diversion channels for the river, looping it back and forth across the plain so that it would offer as many obstacles as possible to an army marching down towards the city. A town that had no such barriers and could not make them was an easy prey, and quickly lost heart if threatened. When the Cnidians, Greek colonists who lived on a peninsula on the coast of Asia Minor, heard that one of Cyrus' generals was ravaging the inland towns, they hastily tried to dig a canal across the narrow isthmus.

A large number of men turned to, but it was observed that the workmen got hurt by splinters of stone in various places about the body, especially the eyes, more often than might have been expected. Indeed, there was something so unnatural about it, that they sent to Delphi to ask what it was that was hindering the work. Their own account is that the Priestess gave them the following answer in iambic verse:

Do not fence off the isthmus; do not dig.
Zeus would have made an island, had he willed it.

Having received their answer, the Cnidians stopped digging, whereupon they were attacked by the Persian army under Harpagus, *and surrendered without a struggle.* (Herodotus, Bk. I, p. 84.)

Commanders very early learned that a body of water, particularly moving water, not only was a strong defensive shield but could be converted into a fearful weapon. A Chinese maxim of the fourth century B.C. warns military commanders never to let an enemy get upstream of them where he could either cut off or pollute their water supply or turn the flood against their army. Many rivers were diverted for precisely this purpose of flooding, and to this day the breaking of a dam above a heavily populated valley is a frightful and highly effective method of warfare. At Thermopylae, the inhabitants are said to have used their famous springs on occasion, diverting the hot waters down over the road to scald would-be invaders.

But the cleverest use of a river as a weapon of war was perhaps made by Cyrus, when he marched against Babylon. The mighty outer walls held up against his siege;

and he could not reach the weaker sections where they ran along the two banks of the river because the Euphrates itself flowed between them, and no soldier could stand in those swift, deep currents. At length, Cyrus thought of a ruse. Secretly leaving a small detachment behind, he suddenly marched his main army away, up the river. The Babylonians, thinking he had abandoned the siege, fell to celebrating what they thought was their victory, and the whole city gave itself over to merrymaking. The bronze river gates were flung open, the timbers laid on the stone piers, and the two sections of the city joined in a drunken festival. In the meantime, Cyrus reached the artificial lake, and finding its basin nearly empty, proceeded to divert the river into it once again. The flow into Babylon promptly dwindled to a trickle, the Persians left behind walked dry-shod on its bed into the city, and by the time Cyrus got back to Babylon most of its rejoicing inhabitants were dead.

The more usual purpose of drying up stream beds was to cut off the supply of drinking water. The ancient kings were constantly advising their generals to do this in order to bring their intended victims to their knees: "Stop up their wells, that they may thirst" rings through their battle orders with monotonous persistence. Of course, defenders could use the same tricks. When Jerusalem was threatened by Sennacherib, King Hezekiah "took counsel with his princes and his mighty men to stop the waters of the fountains which were without the city . . . So there was gathered much people together, who stopped all the fountains, and the brook that ran through the midst of the land, saying, Why should the kings of Assyria come, and find much water?" (II Chronicles 32:3–4.)

On an earlier occasion, Jehoram of Israel, Jehoshaphat of Judah, and their ally the King of Edom found themselves stranded in the desert approaches to Moab, which they were trying to attack. They sent for Elisha, the prophet, who informed them, "Thus saith the Lord, Make this valley full of ditches. . . . Ye shall not see wind, neither shall ye see rain; yet that valley shall be filled with water, that ye may drink, both ye, and your cattle, and your beasts." (II Kings 3:16–17.) The ditches were dug, and miraculously filled (probably by seepage), and the army moved on to the conquest. It is significant of warfare in those days that Elisha's further instructions included advice about what to do when the battle was won: "Ye shall smite every fenced city, . . . and shall fell every good tree, and stop all wells of water." To desert dwellers, this was smiting indeed.

Probably the reason the allies had got into trouble in the first place was that they had neglected one of the cardinal rules of ancient military science: namely, that every foot soldier must carry a waterskin. When any Persian king went along with his army on a campaign, he was obliged to take for his personal use great quantities of water from the sacred river Choaspes, boiled and stored in silver jars, and hauled by a train of four-wheeled small wagons, since the royal person would be defiled if he drank from any other source. Common soldiers could drink anything, but because in the arid lands of the Middle East there was often no water of any kind to be found on the march, the transport of sufficient amounts was the most serious problem of logistics.

Sometimes they tried to depend on the rivers in their path, with long forced marches between. Xerxes did this on his march to Greece, and his vast army is said to have drunk river after river completely dry. Other commanders kept their armies marching by buying water from the natives of lands through which they moved, but this was a

103

hazardous arrangement which the wiser conquerors tried to avoid. Herodotus tells how armies were supplied by camel train in the desert of Sinai, and even how on one occasion mountaineers made a sort of desert pipe line by stitching together the skins of slaughtered animals; they placed the upper end in a spring and unrolled the "pipe" right down the mountainside, to bring the water to an army in the plain. If a military route was used often, or if a ruler thought it might be, it was usually provided with wells at convenient intervals, like the famous series that Queen Zubaida built centuries later along the pilgrim route from Baghdad to Mecca. In the days of the warring kingdoms, such wells had to be guarded night and day, and this was one of the principal tasks of occupation troops.

To an army on the march in the desert countries, a river was always a welcome sight. But if they were obliged to cross it in order to reach their objective, it could also be a most troublesome obstacle. This was another reason why soldiers always carried waterskins, for if they were emptied and inflated with air they made effective floats. As the empires rose and fell, numberless streams were crossed and recrossed by countless soldiers, each supporting his chest on one of these bladders and kicking his legs for propulsion, from the earliest Mesopotamians to the Spaniards Caesar subjugated, and from whom he learned the trick. The method outlived all the ancient empires: the "Golden Horde" of Genghis Khan used floats in its sweep into China, and that of his grandson, Batu Khan, plunged across the Volga, the Don, the Vistula, and the Danube on skin floats in the campaign that culminated in the capture of Pest in A.D. 1241. In fact, when the great empires foundered and the restless tribes swarmed across their undefended borders, the skin float, in its many adaptations, was the indispensable piece of equipment that enabled them to move women and children, animals, and household goods across the rivers that would otherwise have prevented their migrations. (PLATE 6)

Floats were not the only means of crossing, however. Some rivers could be forded, if one knew the spots where they were shallow enough. Xenophon tells how the Ten Thousand, on their march back to Greece, fought their way through the mountainous country of the Carduchi and finally came down into a broad valley through which flowed the river Centrites, forming the boundary of Armenia. "The Greeks rested here and were glad to see the plain. . . . They felt very pleased, then, as they camped here, with plenty of provisions, and often talked over the hardships they had been through." But their troubles were far from ended, for they discovered that the river was too deep to ford, and soon began to wonder whether this welcome stream was going to turn into a barrier against which they would be trapped to await slaughter at the hands of their pursuers. At the same time, they could see an army gathering on the opposite hills to attack them. Xenophon's tense description of the accidental discovery of a fording place and the rejoicing with which the Greeks crossed and outwitted their enemies underlines as heavily as need be the supreme importance of the river in ancient warfare.

On other occasions the Ten Thousand, who, being Europeans, did not carry waterskins, crossed streams by various makeshifts: they went over the Euphrates once by stuffing their skin tent coverings with hay to make clumsy, but buoyant, floats; and they got through the maze of irrigation ditches and canals near Babylon by cutting down palm trees for footbridges.

One of the most ingenious methods of getting across a river was that adopted by Croesus, the king of Lydia, when he moved his army from one bank of the Halys to the other without actually crossing it. He accomplished this feat by marching his soldiers up to the stream and standing them in close formation facing it along the bank; then he made a cut upstream and diverted the Halys around behind their backs to re-enter its channel downstream of them, so that they could march straight ahead across a dry bed. It is possible that the God of Israel suggested some such method to Moses when his people made their miraculous escape through the divided waters, though a hastily built earthen dam, which could be broken to flood the pursuing Egyptians, may be a more likely explanation.

During the whole period from the rise of the cities to the founding of the first world empire under Cyrus, men crossed and recrossed the rivers of their world, attacking their enemies, building their kingdoms, and buying and selling the goods whose exchange was a condition of their civilization. But though we read most in their records about the uses they made of rivers in warfare and trade, it was the older relationships that actually dominated their existence. Through this whole period of change and development, the primary function of the river remained what it had been in neolithic societies: it was the principal source of the water supply, it was a major source of food in the form of fish, and it was the one indispensable implement of agricultural production. Kings and traders and soldiers may have made the "news" in the warring kingdoms, but the whole structure of society still rested firmly on the shoulders of farmers, who could not support the kingdom unless the kingdom in turn saw to it that water came to their fields. The time had long since passed when a cultivator could manage his own irrigation and drainage; if his fields were to feed armies, not to mention vast populations of miners, priests, accountants, shipwrights, metalworkers, and all the others who did not farm, then organized society had to take over the elaborate and costly waterworks such big production necessitated.

"So there was gathered much people together," as the chronicler of Hezekiah's troubles put it. The things that had to be done in the riverine kingdoms of antiquity were for the most part things that could not possibly be done by a small group. Although a whole tribe or a number of agricultural villages might have been able to furnish sufficient workers to throw up a dike against floodwaters, it could not operate a system of flood warnings up and down the whole Nile Valley. Such undertakings required an organization of society far more elaborate. To defend what the men of a kingdom had built, small bands of warriors were not enough; they had to be welded into armies, in which each man did his assigned job. Thus men were obliged to learn far more about how to co-operate with others than had been necessary in earlier societies, and as their needs increased the co-operating units had to become larger and larger.

Nor was the change a matter of mere size only; the sort of co-operation that was needed brought together men of widely differing skills, interests, and even languages. A system of trade extended over a whole drainage area and beyond could grow up only within the framework of a society in which farmers, miners, smiths of all kinds, merchants, sailors, camel drivers, weavers, fishermen, scribes, and a host of other people could work together. The kingdom, with its uniform standards of weight and measure, its law that applied with equal force to all, and its power to order and carry out the great waterworks on which production depended, provided such a framework. To the king, as the embodiment of society, the farmer had perforce to look for the filling of his ditches, just as the city dweller did for the water that came out of his spigot.

An energetic ruler like Sennacherib of Assyria (705–681 B.C.) devoted the major part of his attention to water control, and a brief summary of his efforts here may serve as a reminder of the role played by early kings in general. Since he lived only a couple of centuries before Cyrus established the first *world* empire, his career represents the culmination of men's achievement in the kingdoms and limited empires. Sennacherib of course had to spend part of his energies on such matters as the stopped-up fountains and dry stream beds with which some of his intended victims prevented his conquests. But most of the time he was concerned about matters much nearer home. Farmers around his capital of Nineveh on the Tigris could not depend, as Egyptian farmers could, on a gentle annual flood that would bring down enough soil and water to last a whole year. The Tigris was often more a hindrance than a help, flooding destructively at the wrong time of year and dwindling away to nothing during the months when the crops needed moisture most. It had to be taken in hand and subdued, its floodwaters collected in huge reservoirs to be let out through sluice gates as needed and guided down through extremely long canals to city and farm land. Since its floods were quite unpredictable and its muddy waters were unsuitable for drinking, the storage facilities had to be supplemented by wells, and by cisterns to catch the occasional driving rains that swept down from the mountains of Persia.

It is not surprising, therefore, that Sennacherib's records are filled, like those of most Mesopotamian kings, with accounts of his battles on a hundred fronts against the drought that constantly threatened his kingdom. His inscriptions, as assembled by M. S. Drower (see "Some Suggestions for Further Reading"), show the other face of this Assyrian who "came down like a wolf on the fold." He built on foundations already ancient—more than a thousand years before his time a canal 400 feet wide had taken Tigris water 200 miles down through Babylonia, for example—but like other kings he elaborated the models of his predecessors. Not content with one canal, he built at least eighteen for the supply of Nineveh alone. The most magnificent of these tapped a tributary of the Greater Zab River and brought its water fifty miles to the capital, coming down a grade calculated with amazing accuracy along the foothills, and passing majestically over an arched aqueduct near Jerwan, high above a stream that cut across its path. Something of the energy of Sennacherib is indicated by an inscription in which he says that this gigantic structure, with all its regulating sluices and storage points, was completed in fifteen months. The Romans themselves could hardly better that record, and until they came on the scene the Assyrian aqueduct must have remained one of the greatest triumphs of engineering in the world.

Sennacherib himself seems to have been keenly interested in engineering problems; at least he takes note of every improvement in the science that comes to his attention. He records with evident satisfaction a *shaduf* that was made to water his palace garden: "That daily there might be an abundant flow of water-of-buckets, I had made copper cables and pails [replacing earlier ones made respectively of reeds and clay], and in place of mud-brick pillars I set up great posts and cross-beams over the well," and various bas-reliefs illustrate experiments with double *shadufs* and with other devices for greater efficiency. He cleaned out old wells, replacing their mud-brick linings with stone. In the search for fresh drinking water, he seems even to have tried making *qanats*, those strange horizontal tunnels which tap sources deep inside hills and bring them flowing in an underground river to an exit in the plain: "I . . . dug three rivers in the Khani mountains, which are above the city Erbil, the abode of the exalted lady, Ishtar, and I made their courses straight." If these "dug rivers" are indeed *qanats*, then the king had good reason to boast that he made them straight, for the problems of driving a tunnel on a direct line, when you must work in the darkness under the earth, are so complicated that they can still sometimes defeat engineers who have all the instruments of modern science to give them their bearings. Incidentally, Erbil is watered today by underground conduits, and some of them contain masonry so ancient that it may well be Sennacherib's.

Sometimes Sennacherib's experiments, while temporarily successful, created problems for the future. In order to arrest the flow of one of his new canals when it reached the end of its usefulness below Nineveh, and at the same time to provide some extra building material for later generations, he hit on the idea of planting reed thickets in the water. Then he seems to have forgotten about them, for when his grandson, Ashur-bani-pal, was ruling in his stead, countrymen came in to Nineveh to complain that the reeds had grown into a jungle which was filled with lions: "Shepherds and herdsmen weep because of the lions, villages are in mourning day and night." It probably took a good bit of effort for Ashur-bani-pal to undo what his clever grandfather had done.

On other occasions, Sennacherib's destructiveness was quite deliberate. To punish Babylon, which had been responsible for the death of one of his sons, he pulled down all the principal buildings in the city. Then, "through the midst of that city I dug canals, I flooded the site with water, and the structure of its very foundations I destroyed . . . So that in days to come, the site of that city and its temples and gods might not be remembered, I completely blotted it out with water-floods and made it like a meadow." But a great city like Babylon was too important, even under Assyrian domination, to be left desolate. Sixty years later Sennacherib's successor, Esarhaddon, was obliged to rebuild it. The whole place had become a vast marsh, apparently, inhabited by fish and wild birds, so that before any rebuilding could be done the land had to be reclaimed. Esarhaddon tells how he went about it: "I mobilized all the artisans of Babylonia . . . Trees and reeds of the brakes they cut down with axes, they pulled up by the roots. The waters of the Euphrates I dammed, from [the city's] midst I shut them off, and into their former channels I directed them."

But by and large, Sennacherib's legacy to his kingdom was a rich one, and completely beneficial. His canals, his aqueduct, his masonry dam across the Khosr River, his wells and cisterns remained to increase the prosperity of Assyria long after his death. Even his private gardens were a national treasure, for though he never created anything to rival Nebuchadnezzar's hanging gardens in Babylon as a tourist attraction, he did acclimatize in his well-watered plots all manner of exotic plants, brought from the four corners, and leave them as a permanent addition to his country's products. He was not a pioneer in such horticultural and botanical experiments. He must often have pondered the inscription of his great predecessor Tiglath-pileser I (1115–1102 B.C.), the first Assyrian to push his conquests to the Mediterranean: "I brought cedars, boxwood, and oak [?] trees from the countries which I have conquered, trees the like of which none of the kings my forefathers had ever planted, and I planted them in the gardens of my land. I took rare garden fruits, not found in my own land, and caused them to flourish in the gardens of Assyria." He must also have heard of the exploits of foreigners who had had a similar passion for botanical collecting. Certainly he would know of one of the most famous ladies of antiquity, Queen Hatshepsut of Egypt (c. 1500 b.c.), for all the world knew how she had sent her sailors on the great voyage to Punt to bring back frankincense trees for the temple gardens. Sargon II, who ruled Assyria immediately before Sennacherib, had provided Nineveh with "a park like to Mount Amanus, in which were set out every tree of the Hittite land, and the fruit-trees of every mountain." Sennacherib took pains to preserve such splendid public works, and to add his own contribution to the treasures of the botanical gardens. "I had all the orchards watered in the hot season, and in winter, a thousand fields of alluvium around and below the city I had men water every year." To the collection in the royal park he added "trees such as grow on the mountains and in Chaldea"; his records even include the earliest known mention of cotton, which he calls "wool-bearing trees." (PLATE 7)

If so busy a monarch ever had time to relax, he must have taken most pleasure in simply sitting quietly in his garden, resting on one of the couches that were set out along the open channels where clear water made a cool and rippling sound. Over his head, mulberries, pomegranates, figs, quinces, and lemons cast their shade, filling the air with perfume, or grapevines coiled over a trellis. Stretching out before him were cultivated beds, where gardeners were testing what herbs and vegetables might be added to the produce of Assyria: Miss Drower's list includes "beetroot, turnip, leek, garlic, onion, cress, mustard, radish, lettuce, aubergine [eggplant], colocynth, cucumber, fennel, fenugreek, coriander, marjoram, rue, mint, rosemary, turmeric, ginger, and saffron." With his flair for mechanics he would be pleased by the sight of the watermen working his new *shaduf,* and he would hear their monotonous chant rising and falling as the beam creaked on its pivot. As a background to this music, he would hear the multiple voice of the city, and could reflect that all that lusty bustle of life continued in its streets because he had kept up the waterworks his fathers had built and had improved and extended them.

At the foot of the city lay the Tigris, its muddy waters crowded with the traffic that made Nineveh great: market gardeners bringing in their vegetables, mountaineers from the north floating downstream on their wine-laden rafts, royal messengers alighting from barges and the sweating oarsmen mopping their brows, and everywhere the clumsy coracles bounding and whirling as they ferried the townsmen from wharf to wharf.

To such a king—and his experience could be duplicated in varying degree in that of most monarchs in the ancient world—it must have seemed that humanity had reached a high peak of accomplishment. Throughout his realm, the conflicts of rival economic interests engendered by the agricultural revolution had been settled. They were not solved forever, but for the time being they were held in check by the only method men yet knew, the method of naked force. The river had been subdued and made to flow at human bidding, and as a result of that conquest men had won wealth and power and knowledge beyond anything that had been dreamed in earlier societies.

Kingdoms accomplished much in the enrichment of human life, in satisfying the need of men for a degree of freedom of action within a community of their fellows. Nevertheless, they had their limitations, and as they grew ever larger and more powerful those limitations became more apparent. A man might journey safely through the whole extent of a kingdom, for example, trading and gossiping and seeing the sights, but once outside the boundaries he could no longer be certain of preserving his gains or even his life. So long as society in a given valley performed its water-controlling tasks, farmers brought bumper crops to market and the whole kingdom rejoiced in a period of prosperity. But when invaders from the hills, ignorant of irrigation techniques, overran the country and allowed the waterworks to fall into disrepair, as the Gutians did in Babylonia around 2180 B.C., the frustrated inhabitants went hungry.

To such problems as these, only one answer suggested itself: the king's rule must be extended farther and farther until it could embrace within its own uniformities all the outsiders in whom his people had any interest. The community, in other words, must become a super-community, and since physical conquest was the only way anyone had thought of to achieve this, the kingdom must become an empire. The time was near when a single man might be able to form into one mental image a concept of the entire civilized world and, given the warlike, tribute-collecting propensities of those days, set about to bring it all under his rule.

CHAPTER V

The River in the Mind

TO THE men of Sennacherib's generation, rivers were much more than sources of water supply for their farms and cities, highways for the transport of goods from kingdom to kingdom, and weapons in their never-ending wars. These were practical uses to which the rivers had been put, services they were forced to perform because to a limited extent men had got the upper hand over them. But the river itself was something more than a pack animal or a tool, something infinitely greater and more mysterious. For during the centuries, as men were learning to make some practical use of the flowing water that made life possible, their minds had been busy with questions that had reached toward the very meaning of existence, and speculation had furnished answers when reason could not.

What was this liquid mass, forever changing and forever the same, this substance that could unfold the green shoot from the seed, this force that could sweep men out of its path and out of existence? Where did it come from, and where did it go? Why could a fish live in it, while a man could not? Why would it give way beneath a man's foot, when it carried so firmly the greater weight of a boat? To most of these questions, and a thousand others, men could give no rational answer. But the river haunted their minds, as it filled their daily lives, and answers of some sort were demanded. It could no longer be taken for granted, as the simple fact of experience it seems to have been for extremely primitive people; too much depended upon it. Relationships had to be established, and since men cannot deal with the unexplained, definitions must exist, whether rational or not.

By the time Sennacherib strolled in his garden, the answers were legion. They were not codified into any logical system of thought; they were sometimes self-contradictory, and the same mind would often accept as a basis for action a mass of conflicting notions which could not possibly be sorted into any logical pattern. But illogical and even absurd as many of their ideas may appear to us to be, they did form, together, a tissue of mental and spiritual relationships which men could use as the basis for what seemed to them intelligent action. The river was a thing which they could apprehend under many aspects, and according to the particular way in which it was conceived it could be approached or fled from, used, placated, or subdued.

When Cyrus the Persian set out for the attack on Babylon (539 B.C.), on the first stage of the conquests that were to bring all the world he knew into one vast empire, he encountered not far from his capital of Susa a river called the Gyndus, whose stream lay across the path of his army, blocking their passage. Herodotus, as usual, gives the liveliest account of what happened.

Cyrus was preparing to cross this river, for which boats were needed, when one of his sacred white horses, a high-spirited creature, entered the water and attempted to swim across but was swept under by the rapid current and drowned. Cyrus was so furious with the river for daring to do such a thing that he swore he would punish it by making it so weak that even a woman could get over in future without difficulty and without wetting her knees. He held up his march against Babylon, divided his army into two parts, marked out on each side of the river a hundred and eighty channels running off from it in various directions, and ordered his men to set to work and dig. Having a vast number of hands employed, he managed to finish the job, but only at the cost of the whole summer wasted. Then, having punished the Gyndus by splitting it into three hundred and sixty separate channels, Cyrus, at the beginning of the following summer, resumed his march to Babylon. (Bk. I, pp. 89–90.)

This "punishment" of a river is not an isolated example. On a later occasion, Cyrus' successor, Xerxes, behaved in a similar way when a storm on the Hellespont ripped to pieces the huge floating bridge his Phoenician and Egyptian engineers had built for his army to march over into Europe. Herodotus, again, tells how Xerxes in a raging passion gave orders that the Hellespont was to be whipped with three hundred lashes, have a pair of fetters thrown into it, and even, some said, be branded with hot irons; and how he ordered the men who were plying the whips to shout as they laid on the lashes, "You salt and bitter stream, your master lays this punishment upon you for injuring him, who never injured you. But Xerxes will cross you, with or without your permission."

117

Such behavior was not a mere whim of proud and head-strong monarchs. In attempting to inflict physical punishment on a river, Cyrus and Xerxes were simply giving expression to one of the earliest concepts of natural phenomena that men had formed. At least as early as the neolithic period and possibly earlier, men had conceived all the objects of nature not as objects but as sentient beings. Trees, stones, rivers were living personalities, endowed like men with wills, desires, frailties, and responsibilities. It was perfectly natural to treat them just as Cyrus and Xerxes did. The only thing curious about the Persian conquerors' attitude is that it should have persisted so long in men's minds, after far more sophisticated ideas had been influencing their actions for centuries, particularly since these very rulers on other occasions based their relationships with rivers on many of those later assumptions. They were Persians, of course, newcomers into civilization, and Herodotus looked down upon their behavior with all the disapproval of the enlightened, rational Greek mind he believed himself to possess. And yet he expresses his contempt by calling Xerxes' orders "a highly presumptuous way of addressing the Hellespont, and typical of a barbarous nation" —words which betray that he held precisely the same animistic notions himself.

The confusion is typical. The mind of ancient man was as capable of holding at one and the same time a conglomeration of contradictory and completely illogical notions as our minds are today; and ancient men were quite as able as we to act on ill-assorted assumptions. When Achilles presented a lock of his hair to the River Spercheios, it is not easy to say whether he was simply treating the river as a fellow creature, as one gives a keepsake to a friend, or whether he was attempting to bribe or pacify some spirit that was not the river but that dwelt in it. The

118

same is true of the custom the ancient Trojans had of throwing live horses into their sacred stream, Scamander, or of the ceremony in which Algonquin Indians hurled tobacco into certain waterfalls. Was it thought that the river wanted the horses or the tobacco, that it could possibly have any use for them? Or was it simply a gesture of respect to a mighty spirit that was immanent in the rushing stream? Did this voluntary gift of a highly prized possession come to have the spiritual value of a sacrifice, whose effect was merely enhanced by the fact that it was of no worth to the recipient? By Homer's time the Trojan custom had been supplanted, officially at least, by the ritual sacrifice of animals on dedicated altars placed along the banks of the stream, which suggests that the river was no longer the abode of a water sprite but had become a god.

Nevertheless, one can never be sure of his footing in the shadowy landscape of the ancient mind. Xerxes' attitude towards the Hellespont seems an example of straightforward animism, until one remembers that the final insult he offered it was the jeering remark: "No one sacrifices to you, and you deserve the neglect by your acrid and muddy waters." On the same campaign, when his army reached the river Strymon,

> the Magi tried to propitiate [it] by a sacrifice of white horses, and after performing many other magical tricks in the hope of winning the river's favour, they crossed it by bridges which they found at Nine Ways, a place in the territory of the Edoni; and when they learnt that Nine Ways was the name of the place, they took nine native boys and nine girls and buried them alive there. (Herodotus, Bk. VII, p. 452.)

Characteristically, Herodotus adds the comment of one

who is superior to all such barbarity: "Burying people alive is a Persian custom; I understand that Xerxes' wife Amestris in her old age did it to fourteen Persian boys of distinguished family, by way of a present which she hoped the supposed god of the underworld would accept instead of herself."

But despite the condescending remarks about "magical tricks" and "supposed gods," the Greeks themselves did not neglect the courtesies due to rivers, under whatever aspect one viewed them. Xenophon, that hardheaded master of military tactics, was always punctilious about ritual and ceremony; in his report, their proper observance figures as matter-of-factly as the distribution of troops and the state of their equipment. In his description of the famous fording of the Centrites, he writes as always with his eye on the essentials, swiftly noting every detail that was *necessary* from a military point of view, and wasting no words on anything extraneous or merely decorative.

On reaching the bank of the river where the ford was, they grounded arms, and then Chirisophus himself first put a ceremonial wreath on his head, threw aside his cloak and took up his arms, telling the rest to follow his example. He ordered the captains to lead their companies across in columns, some on the left and others on the right of him. The soothsayers then cut the throats of the animals over the river [shades of the Magi with their magical tricks!] and meanwhile the enemy were shooting arrows and slinging. However, they were still out of range. The appearance of the victims was pronounced favourable, and then all the soldiers sang the paean and raised the battle-cry, and all the women joined in the cry; for a number of the soldiers had their mistresses with them in the army. Chirisophus and his

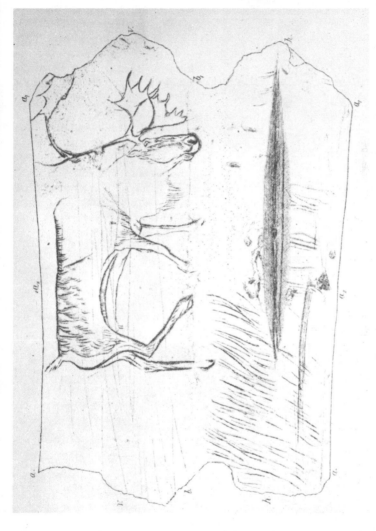

PLATE 1. *The earliest known representation of a river.* Paleolithic engraving on a piece of antler, showing a reindeer grazing beside a stream, found at Kesslerloch near Thaingen, Switzerland, and now in the Rosgartenmuseum, Constance. The object has been provisionally dated at c.25,000-20,000 B.C. So far as is known at present, the attempt to represent a river is unique in paleolithic art, and antedates by thousands of years any later attempt. (Photograph by courtesy of the British Museum)

PLATE 2. *The river as center of the universe.* Babylonian clay tablet, with cuneiform inscription and a map of "the world" (c. eighteenth century B.C.). The Euphrates is shown as "not merely the largest and most obvious detail; it is a huge slash extending from one point on the circular, all-enveloping ocean to the opposite point, bisecting the round disk of the known world: the central fact in the setting of the human drama." (Photograph by courtesy of the British Museum)

PLATE 3. *The river becomes a source of food.* Engraving of trout in glacial clay on the floor of Niaux cavern in the French Pyrenees. The photograph is reproduced through the courtesy of Mme. Windels and the Abbé Breuil, in whose *Four Hundred Centuries of Cave Art* it was originally published.

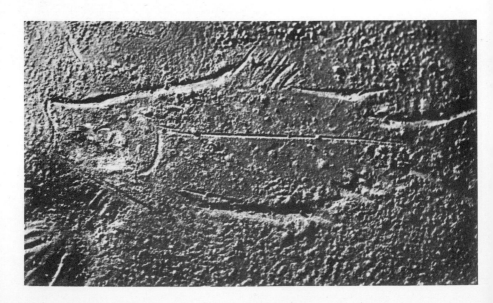

PLATE 4. *The river as the nourisher of crops.* A detail from one of the stone bas-reliefs from the palace at Nineveh, showing a man lifting water from the river by means of a *shaduf* and pouring it into an irrigation ditch. Farther along to the left, two men are using a double *shaduf* to take water from this ditch and distribute it into smaller canals. (Photograph by courtesy of the British Museum)

PLATE 5. *The role of the king in early riverine societies.* Detail of a "great macehead," showing a protodynastic king of Lower Egypt performing the annual ceremony of opening the dikes along the Nile on the "day of breaking the river." His name and title, "Scorpion, son of the Sun," are shown in pictographs in front of his face. (Photograph by courtesy of the Ashmolean Museum)

PLATE 6. *The river in ancient warfare*. Detail from one of the stone bas-reliefs from the palace at Nineveh, showing Assyrian soldiers crossing a stream. The horses swim, and one soldier (lower right-hand corner) swims beside his horse, holding to the rein; the other soldiers support themselves on inflated skin floats. Heavy equipment is carried across the river in a round coracle, propelled by two oarsmen. (Photograph by courtesy of the British Museum)

PLATE 7. *Sennacherib's artificially irrigated gardens.* Bas-relief from Kuyunjik, showing Sennacherib's grandson, Ashur-bani-pal, reclining on a couch under a vine in the artificially irrigated gardens his ancestors had created. Facing the king is his queen, with various attendants. An incidental, and very Assyrian, decoration is the severed head of one of Ashur-bani-pal's enemies, which adorns a branch of the tree in front of the harper. (Photograph by courtesy of the British Museum)

PLATE 8. *The descent of the Ganges.* Detail of a statue of Siva Nataraja (from the Madras Presidency, thirteenth-fourteenth century A.D.). In the wavy tresses of the god sits the tiny figure of Ganga, whom he volunteered to convey to earth. (Photograph by Larkin Bros., reproduced through the courtesy of the Museum van Aziatische Kunst, Amsterdam)

PLATE 9. *The river as divinity.* Statue of the "Great Mother" found by André Parrot at Mari in Syria, and detail. The goddess of fertility wears as her gown a river, in which fish swim upwards toward the "flowing vase" she holds in her hand. The original is in the Museum at Aleppo, and the photographs are reproduced through the courtesy of the Director of Antiquities in North Syria.

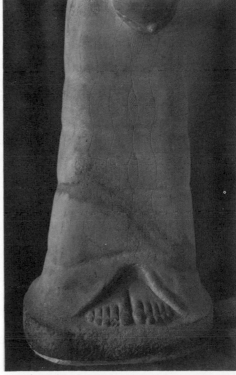

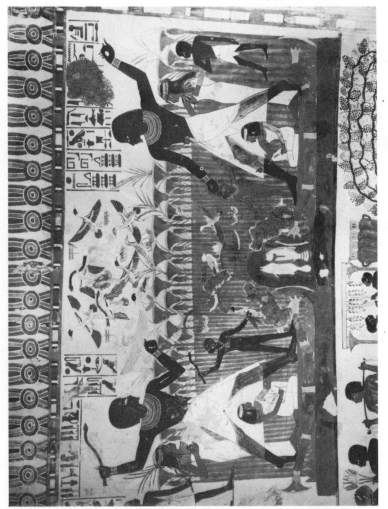

PLATE 10. *The river as place of recreation*. Two noble families of ancient Egypt hunting in the marshes. The boats, although disproportionately small, show clearly the papyrus-bundle construction. The scene is a detail from the elaborate wall paintings in the Tomb of Nakht, Eighteenth Dynasty, c.1400 B.C. (Photograph by courtesy of the Metropolitan Museum of Art, New York)

men then went into the river. (*The Persian Expedition*, Bk. IV, ch. 3.)

I have deliberately extended the quotation to include mention of the camp followers, in order to underline the fact that Xenophon mentions every detail that is relevant to a complete understanding of the commander's job, and only those that are relevant. That mass of women must have given him many headaches, and possibly some entertainment, but he never mentions them except when they impinge on the problem of successful generalship, in this instance by providing that much extra baggage to be carried through the stream. In the same way, he does not talk about his religion, and indeed does not seem to have much, but when a river is to be forded it is incumbent on him to see that the proper beasts are sacrificed in the proper way, with their throats cut "over the water," so that the soothsayers can note how the river receives the blood and can make the correct deductions.

Magic and ritual, superstition, reverence, and worship—all are so intermingled that the various elements cannot be isolated. But wherever rivers have flowed past early communities, men have approached their banks with awe, and the memory of ancient longings clings about them still. Girls on a summer's night still drop their hairpins surreptitiously into streams that once were holy, and not long ago the effigy of the Green George still went to his watery grave in many an English village, when St. George's Day stirred memories of the rites and sacrifices that were needful before men heard of saints. Into the mouths of countless rivers fishermen have thrown one of their comrades to drown, that the grateful stream might fill their nets. When men in the civilizations of ancient India were building their marvelous system of tank irrigation, each of the huge

121

storage ponds was dedicated by a human sacrifice, the body being buried in the tank. And in the solemn festivals with which ancient Egyptians celebrated the annual rise of the Nile, multitudes chanted the ritual song of sacrifice:

Offerings are made to thee,
oxen are slain to thee,
great festivals are kept for thee,
fowls are sacrificed to thee,
beasts of the field are caught for thee,
pure flames are offered to thee.

All this indicates that the concept of divinity came to be associated with rivers at a fairly early stage of human development, that it was so widespread as to suggest a universal impulse, and that once it was accepted men set about establishing the relationships that are appropriate when one is dealing with a god. Some of the most beautiful stories that were told in the ancient world, as well as some of the most gruesome, were woven around the deeds of those mighty deities whose physical manifestation was one or another of the great rivers, as men strove to comprehend the stream and to express its mystery and grandeur. Heroic deeds were performed, and frightful obscenities, in the effort to express men's gratitude for the gifts these gods could bestow, or to appease their terrible wrath when the fit of destructiveness was on them. When children asked why the corn grew ripe, or who made the world, or where the sun goes at night, the gods of the rivers were protagonists in the shining legends they were told. And when poets and sages pondered the ultimate mysteries of birth and death and life's renewal, there were no more evocative symbols to carry the freight of their philosophy.

If you look closely at a statue of the dancing Siva, one of the members of the Hindu trinity of great gods, you may

see a tiny female figure seated in his wavy hair. She is
Ganga, the holy river Ganges, daughter of King Himalaya
and the air nymph Menaka, and the sculptor has placed
her there to commemorate one of the many examples of
Siva's untiring self-sacrifice. When the gods of the Vedic
pantheon took pity on humanity's sinful state, they decided to send Ganga to earth that sins might be washed
away in her purifying stream. But the weight of the mighty
water, falling headlong from the height of heaven, might
very well destroy the whole world. Siva volunteered to take
that weight upon his topknot, and to convey the powerful
goddess downwards by easy stages in a descent that took
a thousand years to accomplish. In the icicles of the
Himalayan cave where the Ganges rises, devout Hindus
see the tresses of Siva, and in the river itself they find
the most powerful symbol of creation and destruction and
purification. (PLATE 8)

Countless are the stories told to explain one or another
aspect of the sacred river. The formation of the delta of
Bengal was a purifying act, for Ganga had divided her
waters into a hundred channels in order that they might
reach the bones of all the sixty thousand members of the
damned house of Sagar and bring them release from their
suffering. But she could also be a jealous and willful goddess: it was told how she had once consented to marry a
mortal, the King Santanu, on the condition that he would
never question or reproach her no matter what she might
do. All went well until the poor king timidly inquired why
she drowned every child that was born to them; to punish
him for his presumption, the haughty goddess abandoned
her spouse without a word.

In one of the *Puranas*, it is written that "All the rivers
are sacred, all flow towards the sea; all are like mothers to
the world, all purge away sins." But it is natural that the

Ganges should be venerated above the rest, for its waters give life to more millions of people than those of any other river except the Yangtze. The people have used it in the most extensive irrigation system in the world, not even excepting that in the Nile Valley. Through a thousand miles of its course, the Ganges has carried one of the heaviest traffic loads of any river. But it is its mystical powers of purification that have been, and are still, most deeply revered. To no other stream does such a vast concourse of pilgrims resort at the stated festivals; thousands perform the special penance of "measuring their length" along appointed stretches of its banks in an arduous series of prostrations; men pray that after death their ashes may be scattered in the stream that can purge away all the evil of their lives. When Bishop Heber visited Benares in 1825, he even saw scores of pilgrims going into the water, each having tied under his arms a pair of large pots with their wide mouths open. The vessels served as temporary floats, to carry the pilgrim into the center of the stream; once safely launched, the man would splash the sacred water into the jars until they were full enough to sink, and pull him gently into eternity, his soul forever pure of earthly stain.

All over the world, men have at certain stages of their development venerated and even deified the rivers they have used. Worshipers of Baal in ancient Palestine knew that their god had a special affinity for springs and streams, and always placed his shrine beside them. The Druids in England regarded as sacred only the rivers that flowed from west to east. The ancient Egyptians, having only one, made it the very center of all their religious thought.

Long before the earliest records were written, the Nile had been worshiped under the form of Hapi, a male god with great hanging female breasts from which gushed the life-giving water. He was usually represented sitting in the shallows of his river and holding over his head a sheaf of lotus plants, their pads and bright blue flowers showing on the surface of the water. Just as the land and all things living had issued originally from the primeval male-female waters, which had shrunk back into a vast circling flood around the earth, so the Nile flowed out from the life-creating stream. Immediately it divided into two courses, one the actual Nile that made Egypt, the other a celestial Nile, a river in the sky, "flowing across the heavens and through the Duat, the world of night and thick darkness, and on that river floats the boat of Ra [the sun-god]." Men knew that the celestial stream was as real as the earthly one, for looking up into the sky at night they could see it arching through the heavens, the luminous river we call the Milky Way.

As the religion of Egypt developed, incorporating into itself foreign concepts and finding ever more subtle explanations for natural phenomena, these basic ideas were modified and enriched, but never superseded. Hapi and Ra, water and sunlight, remained at the center of Egyptian thought, the embodiments of fertility, and of life itself. Many gods were added to the pantheon, Ptah and Amon and Osiris were elevated by turns to the supreme position, but none could achieve the kingship unless he first took on the attributes of Hapi. Because water was imbued with the highest sanctity, the fish who dwelt within it were also sacred, and sacred was the body of anyone drowned. Osiris himself, who in later periods became the most powerful as well as the most popular of the gods, had been drowned, and in the annual inundation he was resurrected, bringing life again to the fields and to men the promise of immortality.

The condition of the immortal soul was one of eternal

transit on the celestial river in the company of Ra. That is why it was essential for the mummified Cheops to be provided with two solar ships, one called Maanjet facing westward for the daytime and the eastward-pointing Mesket to take him through the night. On their spiritual images, his soul would be lifted to heaven, to take his place among the radiant company whose praise forever follows the boat of Ra. And in the wake of Maanjet and Mesket might follow the spirits of innumerable tiny craft, emanated from wooden or clay boat models or even from tomb paintings, on which the souls of lesser men might float in the retinue of their Pharaoh.

In Mesopotamian thought, the gods of the rivers occupied a similarly central position, but because the rivers themselves were less dependable than the calm and beneficent Nile, they were conceived under more violent aspects. For Sumerians and Babylonians, as for Egyptians, the earth and all its offspring had issued originally from Apsu, the great deep that encircled the world. It was the source and parent of Euphrates and Tigris, and the home of Ea, who was paradoxically the god of sweet waters, and hence the patron of irrigation. Because water "avoids rather than surmounts obstacles," Ea was as wily as the snake, who was also, like water, a symbol of fertility; he was therefore worshiped as a god of wisdom, who taught men crafts that demanded cunning and skill. In the zodiac, his goat-fish sign still survives as Capricorn.

Through all the elaborations of religious speculation in Mesopotamia, Ea maintained a central role. But there was far more variety and even contradiction in Mesopotamian concepts than in Egyptian ones, for good historical reasons. Egypt was from very early times a unified country with a homogeneous civilization, so sure of its values that the very word for "Egyptian" was "human being," while "foreigner" meant literally nonhuman. In the valley of the Twin Rivers, by contrast, there was a much longer period of rivalry among city-states, each with its own gods, followed by an enormous stretch of history in which one kingdom after another rose to a position of dominance. Each time, the dominant group was a different people, with different traditions, customs, beliefs, and often a totally distinct language. Mesopotamia became a kind of melting pot into which disparate elements were repeatedly poured, and the story of the Tower of Babel is perhaps the most vivid image of its diversity. Ea, for example, was originally the chief deity of Eridu, one of the small city-states that arose along the northern shores of the Persian Gulf at the dawn of history. His cult was doubtless spread at periods when Eridu was strong enough to demand tribute from her neighbors, but there was so much vitality in it that it was absorbed into all the later religions and traces persist to this day.

Another concept that took an equally firm hold upon Mesopotamian minds was the story of how the god Ninurta had made the world habitable by building a dam to control Kur, the dragon of primeval waters.

> What by Kur had been dissipated, he [Ninurta]
>   guided and hurled into the Tigris.
> The high waters now passed over the farmland . . .
> The fields produced much grain, the harvest of palm-
>   grove and vineyard was fruitful, . . .
> The lord made mourning disappear from the land, he
>   made good the river of the gods.
>   (Quoted by M. S. Drower. See "Some Sugges-
>   tions for Further Reading.")

Here is the antithesis of most of the stories told of Ea. Flowing waters are not beneficent by nature; they are highly destructive, and unless they are brought under control they will be roaring dragons who will devour men and all their works. It is no accident that the most terrifying racial memory of a natural calamity should be the story of a flood that covered the whole earth, and that it should have been told first in the valleys where the Tigris and Euphrates flow down to the sea. But in the oldest version of this story it is Ea, himself the god of waters, who intercedes with the other gods who are bent on wiping out the entire human race. He it is who gives warning of the coming deluge to Ut-napištim (the Noah of the Sumerian version), and who in his wise benevolence teaches the man how to make a vessel on which a remnant of humanity may find salvation and a second chance.

Through all Mesopotamian thought, whether it is essentially Sumerian, Babylonian, Assyrian, or what not, there runs this double conception of good and evil. The rivers are at one and the same time life-giving and life-destroying, and men's attitude to them is a compound of reverence and terror. Enlil is the storm god, scattering death with the lightning-flash of his whip as the rumble of his chariot wheels makes the whole earth shudder in dread, but he is also the bringer of rain, and food-bearing plants sprout from his generous thighs. The "Great Mother" goddess, who is figured under many names, brought forth monsters as well as gods and men; she is sometimes represented wearing a garment whose wavy folds are the currents of a river, in which fish swim upward towards her breasts, but lightning flashes from her brow and her eyes are the eyes of a demon. (PLATE 9) In Mesopotamian art, from the earliest periods to the latest, there appears the motif of the flowing vase, pouring out its sweet waters for the refreshment of men; but on Akkadian seals and in Assyrian reliefs it is just as likely to be held by a malevolent monster as by a genial god. Even the lovely latecomer into the pantheon, Ishtar, the goddess of love, born like Aphrodite from the ocean spray, was also the cruel and unappeasable goddess of war. Yet without her kindly patronage, it was said,

> no stream is opened, no stream is closed, which brings life;
> no canal is opened, no canal is closed, which gives the wide-dwelling people to drink.

Such gods and goddesses dominated the thought of Mesopotamians, as the two great rivers dominated the lives that were lived under the constant menace of drought or flood. Originally, each of the gods had been the patron of one particular community. From the time of the earliest written records in Sumer, the whole population had been organized into the service of the city-god, whose intermediaries were the priests and whose political representative, the king, was in reality a steward, an overseer divinely appointed to keep the god's affairs in order. By the middle of the third millennium B.C., most of the land was actually owned by the temples. Upon this economic foundation was built what Frankfort has called "a planned society best described as theocratic socialism."

All the citizens, high and low, laboured in the service of the god and fulfilled allotted tasks. All tilled his fields and maintained the dykes and canals required for irrigation. Resources and labour were effectively pooled— seed corn, draught animals, ploughs, and other implements were supplied by the temples. Craftsmen kept this equipment in order and regularly presented a quota of their produce to the temple. The harvest of the god's fields and orchards, gardens and cane-brakes, was likewise stored in the temple and regularly distributed to the community in the form of periodical and special (festival) rations. (*The Art and Architecture of the Ancient Orient*, p. 22.)

This system was gradually modified over the centuries, as the growing political power of the king led to a concentration of economic power in his hands and eventually to his assumption of divine attributes. Naramsin, the grandson of Sargon of Akkad, had himself depicted, around 2200 B.C., as a living god, crowned with sacred horns. In Egypt a similar development led, by about 1500 B.C., to the stage where the temples owned almost one third of the land and one fifth of the inhabitants, while the Pharaonic priest-king had already become a god. In other words, in the worship of the great fertility gods of earth and its rivers were laid the foundations on which the sprawling world empires were to be built: the slave economy, the static social organization, the tribute-collecting governmental machinery—all presided over by one all-powerful mortal ruler whose decrees could not be questioned because he was divine.

While these economic and political patterns were forming, men's minds were busy in many other directions as well. As soon as writing was invented, literature began to flourish, first as men hastened to write down the ancient tales they had previously been obliged to carry in the mind and on the tongue, and then as they went on to invent new ones. Knowledge had expanded enormously since the days of the first drainage and irrigation, with speculation keeping pace as men's newly aroused curiosity struggled to explain the world they lived in. Ancient literature is infused throughout with the passion to know and to understand; that is why it is almost exclusively cast in the form of poetry, in which image and symbol are the primary mode of apprehension.

As the religious legend is an account of accepted dogma, so the poetic myth is an exploration of the unknown. The myth gropes towards an explanation of things, and if its findings are satisfying to men's minds it tends to become crystallized into believed legend. But the myth begins as an attempt to answer a question for which there exists as yet no generally accepted automatic reply. What is death? the myth-making poet inquires, and as his mind probes the mysterious depths of that query it finds security at last, not in a rational, scientific explanation, but in a symbol. The image that gives bodily form to that symbol is drawn from one of the most familiar objects in his world. Death is a river, a boundary between two lives, a sleep like that of the drowned, a refreshment, a terror, an element yielding but sustaining, in which is the fertilizing power of re-birth. Whether it is Lethe or Styx, the celestial Nile, or indeed the Christian symbol of the spiritual Jordan—the "one more river to cross" in the deeply moving Negro song —it is an image which no poet has been able to improve upon. Just as living men depended on the watermen in their little coracles to go from shore to shore of the Tigris or the Euphrates, so the Mesopotamian poets conceived of a mythical ferryman, Arad-Ea, to take their souls across the river of death. An Egyptian worried a good bit about "Look-behind," the surly boatman of the Lily-lake, who would have to be placated if his shadow were to reach the island of the Tree of Life. Because of the similar myth of Charon, practical-minded Greeks placed a coin under the tongue of a dead man so that his soul might pay its fare on the ghostly ferry.

The myth served to answer not only philosophical questions, but very often questions of material fact. The body of verified geographical knowledge, for example, was very small. But men were intensely curious about the size and shape of the earth they inhabited, and there were many myths to account for phenomena that could not be explained in any other way. It is true that through trade and commerce and military campaigning men had gradually learned much about the lands that lay beyond the visible horizons; Sennacherib had seen the Mediterranean, and his precursors for centuries had corresponded with the rulers of Egypt; traders and soldiers had reached the Jaxartes River (the modern Syr Darya), far out on the plains and steppes of Central Asia, and had heard tales there of men who lived still farther north where the rivers turned to ice; explorers had pushed down along the coasts of the Persian Gulf and the Red Sea, and may even have gone right round the Arabian peninsula. But each expansion of the known world brought men to boundaries beyond which lay eternal chaos and deep night. The bounds themselves were often shadowy, but those that were identifiable were generally water: the Jaxartes, the Oxus, the Caspian Sea, the Black Sea, the Mediterranean, and the southern seas; the Nile, and possibly also the Indus River on the east. These rivers and seas form a rough ellipse around the lands in which the ancient civilizations flourished. Whether from some vague apprehension of this fact or for no logical reason at all, when men drew an image of the world in their minds they established its limits in a mythical river, Oceanus, which flowed forever in a wide circling flood around the earth.

Mythology was also called on to explain puzzling aspects of actual and well-known rivers. Why did the Dryas come welling suddenly out of the earth? Surely because it had heard the screams of Hercules when he was burning in the shirt of Nessus, and had gushed forth to give him the relief of its cool waters. How could one explain the mysterious fact that rivers in limestone country suddenly disappear into the earth, to emerge again from some cave mouth miles away? The most popular explanation was a myth like that about the spring at Syracuse, which told how the nymph of the stream Arethusa in distant Elis had begged Artemis to save her from an unwanted suitor, and how the goddess of chastity had opened a subterranean channel through which her pure waters might escape.

Rivers often served, in the old tales, as protectors of the weak and the disinherited. There are many tender stories of the foundling whose mother had entrusted him to the care of some powerful stream, in the hope that it might bear him away to a life where his stigma would be unknown. Such stories rested on bitter fact. Many an unmarried mother or slave girl must have felt that almost any casual finder of a little floating cradle would be able to give its tiny occupant a better chance than she could. The classic story of a happy ending to such a desperate resort is of course that of Moses, lifted from the bulrushes by the daughter of Pharaoh himself; but there must have been thousands of slave babies who were never found by any one, but simply drifted from the river of life to the river of death without ever knowing the degrading interval of slavery. These are not often mentioned in the stories. For the comfort of the distracted mothers, the storytellers nearly always told a tale of good luck and eventual achievement for the abandoned child. In actual fact, Moses was not the only fortunate castaway who turned out to be a genius. One of the most moving, as well as the most ancient, royal inscriptions is that of Sargon of Akkad, the first unifier of Sumeria, who has been called "the first really striking personality to emerge as a historical character from the obscurity of records and archaeological evidence."

My mother was humble; I knew not my father. My father's brother was a dweller in the mountain. My town was Azupirani that is set on the bank of the Euphrates. My humble mother conceived me; secretly brought me to birth; set me in an ark of bulrushes; made fast my door with pitch. She consigned me to the river, which did not overwhelm me. The river carried me along to Akki the irrigator [who] brought me up as his son . . . [and] set me to gardening. During my gardening, lo, the goddess Ishtar loved me, and for fifty-four years the kingship was mine. (Quoted by Seton Lloyd: *Twin Rivers*, p. 33.)

The men of the ancient world sometimes dreamed great dreams, and clothed them in splendid poetry, but for the most part their speculations about rivers, and the relationships they established with them, were concerned with the humdrum facts of their daily living. When large numbers of people gathered into cities, problems of pollution inevitably arose. In order to ensure the purity of their water supply, the city dwellers were not obliged, however, to think out entirely new patterns of behavior based on more enlightened concepts than those they had inherited from their distant ancestors. Deeply ingrained in them were ancient attitudes of superstitious awe towards pure water in any form, convictions that the life-giving fluid contained powerful *mana* which must not in any circumstances suffer defilement.

Among the most diverse primitive communities, the water supply has been *tabu*. To the Ashanti people of Africa, according to Hornell, the lake Busumakwe "is so sacred that no canoe may defile its waters. As a consequence,

134

fishermen throw cast nets from a perilous perch astride of unhewn logs." Many primitive peoples inflict the death penalty on any person who pollutes a stream, and among the Badagas of southern India there are severe punishments for spitting in the fountains or even for drinking from a stream without bowing and giving thanks. Herodotus noted as something of a curiosity the rather extreme lengths to which Babylonians of his time would go in order to avoid polluting a spring or a river; he mentions with some astonishment that no Babylonian would dream of urinating into running water, no matter how far it might be away from any settlement. Long before his day, of course, men in the great centers of civilization had given legal sanction to their practices; in the eighteenth century B.C., Hammurabi's Code had laid down rather elaborate antipollution regulations. But such laws were obeyed almost instinctively by Mesopotamians because belief and custom go deeper than law. One can observe even today the persistence of ageless *tabus:* it is said that the modern "devil-worshipers" of Mesopotamia, the Yezidi, refuse to enter the Moslem baths because all water is so sacred it must not be defiled by the touch of a human body, and that they will not eat fish, which they believe to be born of water.

Among most ancient peoples, water not only was pure in itself but was capable of imparting purity. This is one reason why rivers in the Mediterranean world were so often the haunt of women and the scene of all their mysteries connected with menstruation, marriage, and childbirth. Greek girls at puberty bathed in one of the numerous springs or streams that were named "of the Virgins" (*Partheno-*), and they returned for the ceremonial immersions to purify themselves for religious festivals, especially when they were preparing for the rites of marriage.

135

Associated with the idea of the purifying power of running water was the old conception of its gift of fertility. In many places, barren women bathed in certain streams in the hope of conceiving, and the same hope was in the minds of betrothed girls. There were many stories of virgins who had been impregnated during their ablutions by the god of the stream himself, and these virginal brides were described in the fables sometimes as nymphs and sometimes as the mothers of various heroes and demigods.

In all these charming stories of naiads and pure streams there is of course a core of plain common sense. Water *is* a cleansing agent, and cleanliness is a factor in continuing good health. We may refuse to believe that Achilles' first bath in the river Styx actually made his body invulnerable except for the heel by which his mother held him, but we cannot doubt that the customary first ablution of a newborn baby gives him a good start towards a life unscarred by disease. In the same way, we may doubt that the waters of Alpheios, the River of Leprosy, could actually cure that terrible disease; we may look with pity on the deluded lepers who made their hopeless pilgrimage to the river Anigros, or who sacrificed on the altar of Zeus Leukaios, god of the "white sickness." But our skepticism would be a cruel mockery of the faith that sends thousands of our contemporaries to the healing waters of many famous spas.

Medical practice in Mesopotamia also drew upon the curative power of water, though the available evidence seems to indicate a greater dependence on magic than upon minerals. It does appear that salt, taken with the appropriate charms, was a universal remedy. The most common treatment, however, was the Ea-ritual, in which the water-god was invoked in his role of "the great physician." The body of the patient was first washed in water drawn directly from the Tigris or Euphrates, or from a pure spring; then the priest-doctor made an image of the particular demon who was inflicting the pain, placed it in a tiny boat, and committed it to a sacred stream. As it sank into the water, or floated out of sight, the illness departed from the suffering body. When magic began to be replaced by medicine, the ancient treatments were modified into forms that seemed more scientific, but springs and healing streams still occupied a central role. The cult of the semi-mythical doctor, Aesculapius, in the Graeco-Roman world was usually practiced at spas and water resorts; you can still find at places like Bath the votive tablets left in his honor by grateful sufferers who had found in the warm mineral waters some relief from their pain.

In the mind of ancient man, the river thus assumed multiple aspects, and much of the puzzling complexity of human behavior can be understood if we see it as a series of attempts to work out relationships in harmony with these changing conceptions. That men often looked upon the moving waters with awe is evident, and their reactions varied from the sublime to the grotesque. Philosophy, where it existed, was as deeply indebted as religion. Seeking to inculcate a love of goodness and truth, Confucius sent his disciples to contemplate nature with the remark, "The virtuous take delight in mountains; the wise, in rivers." And Heraclitus did his best to make intelligible his profound concept of change by saying that "the same man cannot cross the same river twice." Slowly the myths and legends, the superstitions and penetrating insights were gathered together, sorted, and classified, to emerge at the end of a long evolutionary process into systems of law and religion, while magic continued to incubate the seeds of scientific thought.

But life in the riverine cities and kingdoms was not entirely filled with work and worry and endless speculation.

Some of it, at least, was given over to pure fun. Long before the sun was up on market days, farmers would be splashing about in the irrigation canals that ran past their land, loading onto their rickety boats the fruits and vegetables they had grown, the reed mats their women had plaited and the earthen pots they hoped to sell to the city folk, shouting to the children to sit down in the boat, seeing that their wives with the babies were safely settled amidships, and finally shoving off and leaping aboard for the great journey to town. Down the maze of twisting waterways they would come, calling out to their neighbors as they came abreast of them in the main canals, loudly praising a prize melon or jeering at the man who had picked his dates too soon. Sometimes a whole group of villagers, who had combined to build a large, swift dinghy, would go darting past, the rowers bent over their oars and shouting in unison with each pull, only to crash against another as they swung out into the river where all the boats from the backwaters were converging. As they came near the city, the bustle and jam of the traffic would thicken, and the farmer would strain to keep his precious cargo afloat as he picked his way through the strange craft jostling all around him. Here he would have to watch out for the fishing fleet lumbering up to the wharves, the weight of their catch pushing the gunwales down to the water and their great nets drying on the masts; and he might almost forget to row as he gaped at the fleet of some visiting nobleman or high official, the elaborately decorated barge leading its flock of attendant craft in a stately procession, with the grubby kitchen boat bringing up the rear. One can see on the modern Ganges a sight very like that which was on the Tigris or the Nile three thousand years ago, when the market draws the whole countryside to the city wharves.

On the days and nights of the big festivals, the rivers

were similarly crowded. Boat races, water carnivals, and the glitter of innumerable lights on shore and stream made the river a place of pleasure and recreation for the whole community. Just as the Thames was the center of London social life in the days when Handel's music floated across the water for the entertainment of George II and his court, so was the Euphrates during the brief splendor of the Babylonian renaissance under Nabopolassar and Nebuchadnezzar, and the Nile when Akhenaton, the most imaginative of the Pharaohs, and his Queen Nefertiti, the most beautiful of women, were leading their tragically inopportune revolution.

The rivers drew men together in communal pleasures, strengthening, no doubt, a sense of individual participation in a larger life that embraced neighbors and strangers, and even foreigners from distant lands wearing their exotic clothes and clacking away in incomprehensible languages. But they also called men away from the busy towns to the sweeter pleasures of solitude. The new economy that had come in with the building of cities made possible a certain amount of real leisure, at least for a few, and the men of the towns had early begun to turn for relaxation and refreshment to those spots where nature was still undisturbed by the noisy intrusion of progress. Some of the most moving paintings on the walls of Egyptian tombs are those in which men tried to immortalize the hours they had spent in their little boats among the reeds of the marsh where their ancestors had hacked out new modes of existence. For the patches of jungle swamp that were left were no longer terror-haunted wildernesses that must be attacked and conquered if men were to survive; they had become quiet retreats, where a man might forget the cares of the countinghouse as he stood poised in his boat, with his wife crouching behind, holding his legs so that he would not fall when he suddenly let fly his throwing stick as the ducks rose with a wild whir of wings from the reeds ahead. It was all very well to provide for a funeral craft on which a man's soul might follow forever the sun-god in his endless journeying, but one often feels, in looking at the walls on which men left their own accounts of their lives, that the memories they cherished most were of those days they spent alone in a real boat with their wives and children, soaking into their naked bodies the heat of an actual sun and feeling underneath them, through the planks on which their bare feet stood, the palpable movement of an actual stream. (PLATE 10)

CHAPTER VI

Streams of Persian Gold

A great god is Ahuramazda, who created this earth, who created yonder sky, who created man, who created happiness for man, who made Darius king, one king of many, one lord of many.

I am Darius the Great King, King of Kings, King of countries containing all kinds of men, King in this great earth far and wide, son of Hystaspes, an Achaemenian, a Persian, son of a Persian, an Aryan, having Aryan lineage.

Saith Darius the King: By the favour of Ahuramazda these are the countries which I seized outside of Persia; I ruled over them; they bore tribute to me, what was said to them by me, that they did; my law—that held them firm: Media, Elam, Parthia, Aria, Bactria, Sogdiana, Chorasmia, Drangiana, Arachosia, Sattagydia, Gandara, Sind, Amyrgian Scythians, Scythians with pointed caps, Babylonia, Assyria, Arabia, Egypt, Armenia, Cappadocia, Sardia, Ionia, Scythians who are across the sea, Skudra, petasos-wearing Ionians, Libyans, Ethiopians, men of Maka, Carians.

Saith Darius the King: Much that was ill-done, that I made good. Provinces were in commotion; one man was smiting another. The following I brought about, that the one does not smite the other at all, each one is in his place. My law—of that they feel fear, so that the stronger does not smite nor destroy the weak. (Inscription on Darius' tomb, quoted by Ghirshman: *Iran,* pp. 153–4.)

I T W A S the sixth century B.C., some two hundred years since Sennacherib had puttered in his garden, admiring his double *shaduf* and his wool-bearing trees. Assyrian dam builders had long since departed from Arabia, the plant hunters had been recalled from Amanus and the merchants had drifted back from their trading posts in Asia Minor. Under repeated blows from the newly organized power of Medes and Scythians, the Assyrian empire had shrunk back upon its home base astride the Tigris, control of whose waters had once made it great. When Nineveh finally toppled, the "center of the world" had shifted back, as it always had before on such occasions, to another city on the bank of one of the great rivers. This time it was Babylon on the Euphrates once again, the town Esarhaddon had reconstructed on Sennacherib's ruins. There for a brief space Nabopolassar and Nebuchadnezzar had contrived a feverish splendor, with their hanging gardens, their bronze gates and stone-piered bridges, and their elaborate system of water defenses.

But already the Hebrew prophets were crying woe to "that great city Babylon, that mighty city," and its role as the wonder and the terror of the world was quickly played. Perhaps the prophets instinctively realized that the river-controlling city, like its rulers, had been weighed in the balance of history and found wanting. For the ancient riverine capitals could no longer, by their mere position, dominate as they had once done.

When wealth had been measured primarily by the food that could be raised on properly drained and irrigated land, a town on the bank of a large river could become a rich city-state merely by developing the agricultural possibilities of the plain. Expansion up- and down-river could transform it into the capital of a thriving kingdom, and as the traders' boats penetrated farther and farther up the tributaries the kingdom could grow into a small empire, in which the strategically placed city ruled over all the various peoples in the entire drainage system. This, however, was about the extent of all the empires before the Persians. Even at the periods of its widest expansion, the Egyptian empire had been essentially a Nile kingdom, just as the Akkadian, Babylonian, and Assyrian empires had been mostly limited to the great drainage system of the Twin Rivers.

It is true that they had all reached out for wealth that lay beyond their watersheds, especially in the coastal strip between the Jordan Rift and the Mediterranean. With ocean-going vessels, the art of which was largely a Phoenician monopoly, the Pharaohs could communicate and trade with the bustling coastal towns, and at times they could send conquering expeditions and temporarily occupy Palestine and Syria. They also used the first international highway ever constructed, a caravan route across Sinai and up through Palestine to Asia Minor. But they were never able to weld any part of Asia into a genuine Egyptian community, bound to the imperial power by a common official language, a common economy, and a common civilization. The Mesopotamian monarchs were no more successful, for the desert was as effective a barrier to them as the sea to the Egyptians. Only the later Assyrians began to build the necessary system of overland communications, and they began too late. By the time it was well enough organized to take the place of the rivers that had held the earlier kingdoms together, the city on the Tigris had passed its zenith and Sennacherib's successors were being hounded out of history by a new power in the east who could think in terms of geographical space rather than in terms of a continuous network of flowing waters. The Achaemenian empire of the Persians, founded by Cyrus (559–530 B.C.) and consolidated by Darius (522–486 B.C.), was the first that was not based on the control of a single river system.

Cyrus and Darius did not themselves bring about this radical change in the relationship between men and rivers, of course; they merely appeared on the scene at the moment when a long series of evolutionary shifts and changes that had been accumulating over a period of centuries had reached a culminating point, and human society was ready for a regrouping of its energies which would take account of them. The individual river system was still a powerful factor in drawing human beings into community, but it was no longer the only one. Now there were a number of new tools which could be used to build a unified society on the grand scale. Subtly reaching out across the watersheds, irresistibly linking Euphrates with Nile, Jordan with Oxus (the modern Amu Darya), and even Indus with Danube, a variety of inventions, devices, attitudes, and human activities had begun to operate in human affairs. And the total effect of these new factors was to prepare the way for a kind of international community which had not existed before.

In the palace which he built at Susa around 490 B.C.,

144

Darius put up an inscription that gives some broad hints about the nature of his cosmopolitan empire and the forces that held it together.

This is the palace which at Susa I erected. From afar its ornamentation was brought. Down the earth was dug until rock-bottom I reached. When the excavation was made, rubble was packed down, one part 40 ells in depth, the other 20 ells in depth. On that rubble a palace I erected.

And that the earth was dug down, and that the rubble was packed down, and that the [sun-dried] brick was moulded, the Babylonian folk, it did that.

The cedar timber, this—a mountain named Lebanon —from there it was brought; the Assyrian folk, it brought it to Babylon; from Babylon the Carians and Ionians brought it to Susa.

The yaka wood from Gandara was brought and from Carmania.

The gold from Sardia and Bactria was brought, which was used here.

The stone—lapis-lazuli and cornelian—which was used here, this from Sogdiana was brought.

The stone—turquoise—this from Chorasmia was brought which was used here.

The silver and the copper [some scholars translate *ebony*] from Egypt was brought.

The ornamentation with which the wall was adorned, that from Ionia was brought.

The ivory which was used here, from Ethiopia and from Sind and from Arachosia was brought.

The stone pillars which here were used—a place named Abiradush, in Uja [Elam]—from there were brought.

The stone-cutters who wrought the stone, those were

145

Ionians and Sardians. The goldsmiths who wrought
the gold, those were Medes and Egyptians. The men
who wrought the *ishmalu* [wood], those were Sardians and Egyptians. The men who wrought the
baked brick, those were Babylonians. The men who
adorned the wall, those were Medes and Egyptians.
Says Darius the King; At Susa, here, a splendid task was
performed; very splendidly did it turn out.
May Ahuramazda protect me; and Hystaspes who is my
father; and my country.
    (Quoted by Frankfort: *The Art and Architecture of
    the Ancient Orient,* pp. 214–5.)

The longer one ponders this astonishing inscription, the
more clear becomes its evidence of a profound alteration
in human relationships. An incursion of upland people into
the old valley centers was of course nothing new under the
sun; it had occurred repeatedly, time out of mind. But
when it had happened in earlier periods, the invaders had
seldom been able to consolidate their conquests. Now a
people from the dry plateaus of Iran were able, in a relatively few years, not only to take over a decadent river-
based empire, but to expand their dominion over virtually
all the lands that men in their day had ever heard of. They
had quickly organized what seemed to be the whole world
of man into a tightly knit community. Yet this achievement is only the most obvious of the novelties Darius' inscription records.

Susa itself is a most surprising place for the seat of a
powerful government. Instead of being a great and ancient
city on the middle reaches of some mighty stream, it was
a poky little provincial town, a name never before mentioned in fashionable talk or commercial conferences, of
no interest to the people who ran the world's affairs. True,

four rivers connected it with the sea, but though the Choaspes was holy (to the locals) and the Kafur was big enough to be diverted into a moat around Darius' palace, they were all of them thin, short, and uncertain, and capable of dominating nothing. Darius dwelt at Susa because it pleased him to do so, and where the Great King was, there was the center. Not even Susa was a permanent capital; the Achaemenians were always moving their capital, from Susa to Ecbatana (Hamadan) and back again, and when these lost their charm they built entirely new splendid capitals in the middle of nowhere, like Pasargadae or Persepolis. Theirs was an empire of a new kind, and its shifting capital was symbolic, not of uncertainty in aim or vacillation in policy, but of a flexibility in the exercise of power which had been unknown before. Because the river had surrendered some of its dominance over men's lives, they were the first great monarchs who *could* move the seat of their government blithely around from pillar to post, the first who were not bound of necessity to a major river because it was the one dominant unifying force that could hold their empire together.

The very extent of that empire was something new under the sun, for it spread into lands where civilization had not penetrated before, and drew to its center the products and skills of peoples whose names had been unknown. The mighty place names of antiquity—Egypt, Babylonia, Assyria—are in Darius' list, and their long familiar border regions like Arabia, Armenia, Cappadocia, Libya, Ethiopia, Elam, and Media. But they are leveled down to make room for a host of strange and barbarous names that have emerged suddenly into recorded history: tribes like the Sattagydae and Arachosians, occupying what we call Afghanistan; from high up on the Kabul River, guarding the passes through the Hindu Kush, the Gandarii who earned

147

their place in the record by felling yaka wood and shipping it to Susa; Bactrians just over the passes on the upper reaches of the Oxus, and Sogdi on its lower courses as it nears the Aral Sea, buying their way into history with gold and cornelian and lapis-lazuli; Chorasmians shipping turquoise from their desert land between Oxus and Caspian; and three widely separated peoples so little known that they are all called Scythians, though some live near the Bactrians, some wear pointed caps and dwell in bitter plains north of the Caspian, and the most outlandish of all are simply "beyond the sea" in the cold and murky lowland between Danube and Don. Finally there are the city-states of Greece with their maritime colonies, and their populations of quick-witted, clever traders, and craftsmen who were skilled above all men in stone-cutting. At Susa they were merely practicing for the Parthenon they would build a century and a half later to the glory of their own Athens; before two centuries were out their petasos-wearing brethren would have the whole of Darius' empire in their own hands.

What held this vast community together, making it possible for men and their wares to move safely from one end of it to the other and for thousands of workers and overseers, traders, shippers, contractors, artisans, and slaves to join forces so successfully as they did at Susa? Darius thought that the cement of empire was "my law—that held them firm." But law, even that of the Medes and the Persians, is a result and not a cause. The actions of the Great King speak on the subject more eloquently than his words, and it has been well observed that everything he did had a commercial aim. The world as the Achaemenians knew it had at last reached a stage in which international commerce could be organized on a world scale, and this is precisely what they did.

Of the various factors which helped to bring about the situation Darius exploited, one of the most effective was a device Cyrus had heard about when he conquered Lydia (546 B.C.). Croesus, the king of that Greek country, not only knew how to move an army across the Halys River without actually crossing it; he knew something vastly more important, namely, how to move commerce back and forth over boundaries across which it was difficult if not impossible to transport heavy goods. According to the legend Croesus had the gift of turning whatever he touched to gold, a convenient form of wealth in which a single swimmer can transport across a river the equivalent of several tons of goods. The fact behind the story is that although various rulers had struck small silver coins during the previous century, Croesus was the first to set up a true monetary system, using both gold and silver coinage.

Before his time, payments had been made in kind. Pharaohs wanting timber from Lebanon had to pay with shiploads of grain; the Sargonids could get copper or wine only by giving textiles or barley or dried fish; while the trader up in the wilds of Europe had to place bales of cloth, stacks of iron weapons and tools, or bright-colored knickknacks from sophisticated Mediterranean shops in an open place beside a stream, and then hide in the nearby forest all night hoping that the shy savages would lay beside his wares a more valuable pile of furs or a hoard of precious amber in token that they were willing to exchange. In Croesus the traveling salesman found his patron saint. Coinage had made him rich, and when it was quickly adopted by the Persians it helped to usher in the most brilliant period of commerce the ancient world had ever known. Ignoring the mountains and the rivers, the deserts and the seas that had limited earlier trade, thin bits of metal now flowed in steady, tinkling streams from Sind to Attica, and from Ethiopia to the banks of the Jaxartes.

The trade it stimulated was not only far greater in quantity than at any earlier time, but was significantly different in the kind of goods involved. Luxuries were no longer the main items: the bulk of shipments were ordinary everyday things like pots and pans, furniture, and cheap clothing. There was an enormous traffic in dried fish, a staple of all ancient diets. The novelties among Persian exports were such utilitarian things as domestic fowl, white doves, and lucerne grass, all of which they introduced into Europe, to the abiding benefit of European agriculture. It was farmers also who profited by their introduction of sesame into Egypt, their encouragement of the spread of pistachio cultivation into Asia Minor and Greece, and their importation into Mesopotamia itself of rice from India. It is no wonder that ordinary people began to be more prosperous and to feel more comfortable under the Persians than they had in previous dispensations.

To assist in the circulation of money, the first genuine private banks arose, soon taking over the limited banking activities that had occasionally been carried on by temples or wealthy princes, and extending them to include most of the operations of modern banking houses. Ghirshman describes a bank run by the descendants of Egibi of Babylon and another known as "Murashu and Sons" at Nippur, with their deposits and floating loans, their capital investments in fields, slaves, cattle, and trading boats, their leases, their waterworks, and their monopolies in fishing and brewing which they farmed out at a profit.

With such assistance, the gold moved swiftly, stirring up in its wake a ferment of manufacturing, jobbing, and retailing. Naturally, much of it flowed into the royal treasuries, in the form of taxes and direct tribute. Where the earlier limited empires had collected grain tribute, the Persians collected gold. They spent it again to build roads and waterworks, to support a vast administrative machinery, to finance military and commercial expeditions, and above all to buy control of men they could not conquer by force of arms. Persian gold became a new and sinister weapon of diplomacy. It was used to blackmail kingdoms, to purchase allies, and to corrupt the politics of the Greek city-states so thoroughly that for over a century they squandered wealth and blood in a series of internecine wars, which almost cost them the chance of their magnificent moment in history.

But money was not the only thing that could now pass freely from basin to basin, across deserts, and over seas. The things men chiefly bought and sold were more easily transportable than the stuff their ancestors had bartered, and at the same time the means of transport had improved greatly. Ships of 100 to 200 tons were now sailing on the greater rivers, and even 500-ton vessels were being built for ocean transport. Their masters were using ship's papers and were employing sailors who were strictly graded according to their skills. Grain ships sailed across the Black Sea and through the Straits, bringing wheat from the Danubian plains to Greece and the Asia Minor cities, and freighters of all sorts swarmed in the eastern Mediterranean. Instead of the occasional and almost fabulous voyage of a few Egyptian ships to Punt, there was now a heavy traffic up and down the Red Sea.

Darius saw the immense commercial possibilities that would open if he could connect the Mediterranean-Black Sea traffic with Arabia and the east coast of Africa, and also with his eastern dominions. When, on one of his early campaigns, he reached the point where the Kabul River joins the Indus, he stopped there long enough to build a fleet. When it was seaworthy, he put it in command of a Greek named Scylax, who came from the town of Caryanda in Asia Minor, and gave him orders to take it down the Indus and sail westward on the seas until he should reach Egypt. It was an order which must have had the same terrifying effect on the crew as Columbus' doggedness had on his; for all they knew, they might be sailing straight into Oceanus, where they would be swept in an endless voyage round and round a world they could never reach again. But Darius knew that Indian spices had been sold in the west and apparently suspected that Arab sailors had taken them, though no one had been able to worm their trade secrets out of that closemouthed people. Nevertheless, Scylax sailed, and thirty months later he turned up at the northern end of the Red Sea. Soon after this, Darius discovered an unfinished canal in Egypt, said to have been started by a Pharaoh named Necho in an attempt to connect the Nile with the Bitter Lakes, and thence with the Red Sea. According to the story, Necho had given up the job on the warning of an oracle that it would bring him bad luck. Darius seriously considered finishing it, in order to make a direct water route from the Mediterranean to Persia and India, but his engineers seem to have had more influence on him than an Egyptian oracle could: they apparently warned him that since the elevation of the Red Sea was higher than that of the lower Nile, salt water coming into the canal might ruin the river. Darius gave up and used an overland portage. From his time on, however, men dreamed of a Suez canal.

While the sea lanes were being opened from one end of the empire to the other, Darius and Xerxes and their successors were building a network of roads over which journeys of the same extent could be made by land. Some of them were totally new, like the highway that ran from

Susa to Persepolis, with its fork that goes up through the Persian Gates onto the central plateau, or the northward road the court followed when it moved from Susa to Ecbatana. From the latter point, a new road stretched eastward to the place where Scylax had started his voyage, with one branch going from there up the Kabul toward the passes and another following the main river down into India. Westward from Ecbatana, the old road to Babylon was improved, as was the great highway extending from Babylon by way of Carchemish clear into Egypt. But probably the greatest of all the Persian highways was the Royal Road. As Ghirshman describes it, this splendid thoroughfare

> went [northwest] from Susa, crossed the Tigris below Arbela, passed by Harran and ended at Sardis, whence it was extended to Ephesus. One thousand six hundred and seventy-seven miles long, it was divided into one hundred and eleven post-stations, each with relays of fresh horses for royal couriers. According to the ancient historians, the caravans took ninety days to travel this road from end to end, while the royal convoys covered it in a week. (*Iran*, p. 145.)

Merchants were quick to realize the value of such trade routes. Now that the drivers had learned to tie clumsy coverings on to the feet of their animals when the going was rough, the patient beasts could carry merchandise on the roads over mountains and marshy valleys, in sunshine or rain. Rivers were no longer the only avenues of trade. The boats still plied in their hundreds up and down the Tigris and Euphrates, cedar logs lashed together into rafts still floated down from the Lebanon to Byblos and Tyre, and the Nile was still almost the only way of reaching Memphis. But the rivers were now only links in a system of transportation in which sea routes and overland trails were of at least equal importance.

Over this complex of itineraries, men moved at will throughout the empire, able to buy transportation with the magical bits of silver and gold they could carry on their persons, and able to bargain wherever they might be, so long as they could speak Aramaic. For another of the sensible contrivances of the Achaemenians was their adoption of this language of the Jews as a *lingua franca,* which all officials were required to speak and in which all business could be understandably conducted. It is a mark of their particular kind of genius that they did not try to impose their own tongue on the conquered peoples, but chose rather a language that was already known in the market places of Asia Minor and Mesopotamia. Confusion of tongues had finally prevented the completion of the Tower of Babel, but the multilingual group who toiled at Susa and Persepolis were able to finish their job because they could all talk with one another. Standardization went even further: the Persepolis tablets describe an imperial public works organization which recruited and managed workers and undertook constructions throughout the entire empire.

Oddly enough, these organizing geniuses made no effort to establish a universal religion. Despite their own firm devotion to Ahuramazda, they never tried to force anyone else to worship him, nor did they favor any one foreign deity above another. Although they flourished at a time when men's desire for unity was expressing itself, among other ways, in a yearning for monotheism and universality of faith, they took no account of its appeal. Religions that were later to bring men from the ends of the earth into communion and a sense of brotherhood, like Buddhism or Jainism or Judaism, had already produced their great prophets, just as the Persians' own system had produced Zoroaster; philosophy was replacing religion with the ethical system of Confucius in China, and was soon to flower in the schools of Greece. There was also a long tradition of self-deification by which rulers had reinforced their power, and which later emperors were to revive. But the Achaemenians remained peculiarly indifferent to the unifying power of a state religion. Perhaps they realized that although providing a common language may be good for business, meddling with men's souls is not. People were at liberty to worship sticks or stones, or rivers, if they pleased, and, as we have seen, even the rulers themselves were perfectly willing to sacrifice to foreign streams whenever such action might possibly further their own interests.

With Darius, "everything had a commercial aim," and the system he created to foster international commerce was to persist long after his successors had lost the political control of it. Alexander of Macedon, the first non-Persian who attempted to rule their entire empire, and the only one who succeeded, strove to alter nothing in their system, but merely to strengthen it where it had grown weak. He looked upon himself not as a rebel against the Persian system, but as its savior: a true successor of the Achaemenians, a man who had grown up in the "one world" they had created and whose aspiration was simply to control it and make it more unified than ever. The ruling house had grown decadent, and in a series of conquests (336–323 B.C.) extending over their entire domains and even beyond, Alexander swept them forever from the stage of history. But there was never any question of destroying what they had built; in fact, his intentions were exactly the opposite.

The later Achaemenians had weakly allowed their satraps in many of the provinces to issue a local coinage. Alexander stopped this practice, and reinstated a single universal coinage such as Darius had issued. Aramaic remained the *lingua franca* of trade; only later was its unifying function gradually taken over by Greek. In order to strengthen loyalty to the throne of the Great King, Alexander had himself deified. But his intentions are most clearly shown in the ideas he had for improving trade.

Under Darius and his successors, the eastern boundary of the empire had been the Indus. After foraging up into Central Asia as far as the Jaxartes, Alexander marched southward over the passes, came down the Kabul River, and entered the Indus Valley. He crossed the river on a bridge of boats and raided deep into the Punjab. Here he found rich trading cities like Taxila, sitting astride an overland route that came down from Kashgar in Central Asia through enormously high passes, importing goods and passing them on to a mysterious kingdom somewhere far to the east. He was pushing on towards this eastern land when his soldiers finally announced that they would go no farther, and regretfully Alexander was forced to abandon his quest.

But he had learned enough of Indian trade to guess its value, for when he reached the Indus again, he did exactly what Darius had done two hundred years earlier. Nearchus was ordered to build a fleet, and to retrace the voyage of Scylax as far as the Persian Gulf, staying close to the coast that stretched westward from the mouth of the river. At the same time, Alexander divided his army, sending half his men northward to pick up the great road to Susa and taking the other half with him on a march along the coast, where he could keep in some sort of touch with the fleet.

It is evident that Alexander and Nearchus were trying to establish a trade route, mostly by water, that would pass through the heart of the empire to connect its uttermost regions. From Susa, where Nearchus finally joined the young king and where they immediately set about building wharves, there was of course the great Royal Road leading almost to the Syrian coast. But river transport is cheaper and safer than caravans, and Nearchus was soon sent to explore the marshy northern end of the Gulf; the purpose was to find a usable channel up one of the treacherous, silt-choked mouths of the Euphrates and into the main stream above the delta. Alexander himself moved up to Babylon, where he spent the last few months of his life feverishly strengthening the administration of the empire and planning for its future.

One of his chief concerns was a thorough renovation of the canals throughout Mesopotamia, and this must have been largely in the interests of navigation. When he had first entered the Euphrates Valley, some twelve years earlier, he had seen near the river the great depression in which Lake Habbaniya lies, and had conceived the brilliant scheme of diverting floodwater into it, both in order to protect downstream cities and to keep the canals and river channels navigable. Alexander did not live to accomplish this project; only in our own time is it being carried out. His plan, however, looks like part of a great proposal to develop a trade route along the shortest waterway between India and the Mediterranean countries. If goods could travel by boat down the Indus, along the coast to the Persian Gulf, and then up the Euphrates to its head of navigation before being transshipped, they could be sold in Syria, Greece, and even in Egypt for less than those moving by any land route. Mediterranean and even Black Sea products could of course travel back on the same route to be exchanged.

As a matter of fact, that is exactly the route by which a great deal of merchandise did move in later periods. If Alexander had lived to establish a dynasty that could have

157

held the Achaemenian empire together, there seems little doubt that it would have become the main, if not the only, artery of east-west trade. Instead, when the empire was divided into three parts, and later on when all its western regions were overrun by a new empire from outside altogether, that "lifeline of trade" became the prime objective of all empire builders.

When Alexander died in Babylon, his various generals began a struggle to succeed him. After some thirty years, they reached a settlement: Ptolemy established a Greek dynasty in Egypt which claimed control of northern Arabia and Palestine as well; a line of Macedonian rulers asserted their claim to Asia Minor, the Black Sea coasts, and all of Greece. The strongest of the generals, Seleucus, took what seemed obviously the best: all the heartland of the old Persian empire, stretching from Syria northeastward across Mesopotamia and Iran to the Oxus and Jaxartes, and southeastward to the Indus. This gave the Macedonians and the Ptolemies access to the continents stretching back north and south of the Mediterranean, inhabited by barbarians who were potential customers or slaves. But it gave the Seleucids the vital water route, and opened for them a gateway into a fabulous world.

Far to the east of the Indus, Alexander had heard of a network of streams feeding into a great river which flowed eastward down a seemingly endless plain to some unknown sea, and had been told stories of a wonderfully rich kingdom in its valley. When Seleucus turned his attention eastwards, he found to his surprise that the kingdom had suddenly become an empire, whose ruler was acknowledged right up to the Indus itself. He prudently accepted the situation, made a treaty of peace, and sent one Megasthenes as an ambassador to find out what manner of men these new imperialists were. The report Megasthenes brought back was almost as startling to men of his day as those of Columbus were to be to his contemporaries.

Men in the Achaemenian world had always supposed that the Great King held sway over the whole of the civilized world; beyond his domains lay only the lands of the barbarians. Now Megasthenes could tell them that the Ganges Valley was occupied by people as highly civilized as themselves, people who practiced irrigation with a skill at least equal to anything known in Mesopotamia, ruled by an emperor named Chandragupta Maurya whose court was as brilliant as that of Seleucus. They were a riverine people, who had supplemented the natural waterways with a maze of navigable canals, through which loaded boats moved in endless procession. Although Megasthenes did not learn much about the sources of their wealth, apart from their flourishing agriculture, we know today that the Indians were already carrying on a lively overseas trade from the mouths of the Ganges with Burma, Malay, and even with Ceylon, and that at the same time they were sending overland caravans northward into Central Asia (up the Indus and over the Hindu Kush) and southward to the spice country of Malabar. But the ambassador did observe some of the results of this trade. Chandragupta's subjects wore diaphanous robes spun of cotton and dyed with indigo, and rubies in their turbans red as boar's blood. They used exotic perfumes like nard and sandalwood, and seasoned their food with cinnamon, and with spices still more rare which no Greek had ever tasted. Above all, they had pepper, a spice that was destined to be one of the most precious articles of world commerce for the next two thousand years, far more highly valued by Roman epicure and Elizabethan freebooter than frankincense had ever been by the Pharaohs.

The introduction of such luxury goods into the Mediterranean lands changed again the character of international trade. The cheap, homely articles that had predominated in the markets when Darius controlled them were replaced by rare and costly treasures from India. Through their importation and resale to lands farther west, the Seleucids grew rich. At the same time, the rarities brought such fantastic prices that the value of ordinary gold and silver fell by fifty per cent, a phenomenon that has occurred only one other time in human history—when Spanish galleons flooded Europe with the looted treasure of the Incas.

Since they had good relations with the Maurya empire and controlled the most direct trade route to the west, the Hellenized Persians naturally became the middlemen through whom westerners must buy. As such, they were not loved. They also became, equally naturally, the object of envy on the part of all the restless nomadic peoples on their northeastern borders, who wanted to take over their profitable function. Much of the history of the rise and fall of empires in the Mediterranean basin and Southwest Asia, from the time of Alexander until the Arabs in the seventh Christian century swept them all away, focuses on the attempts of these buyers and would-be middlemen either to seize the vital trade route for themselves or to find alternative routes by which they could by-pass the Persians.

Two possible alternatives suggested themselves. The first would be a sea route such as Scylax had explored, from India directly across to the Arabian coast and along it to the Red Sea where cargoes could be unloaded on Egyptian soil. The other, which was attempted later, would use the Indus-Hindu Kush road to the valley of the Oxus River in Central Asia and then swing west to the Caspian Sea, passing north of the Persian-held lands. Once Indian goods reached the Caspian and crossed in boats to its western shore, there was a certain valley cutting through the Caucasus Mountains in which two small and otherwise unimportant rivers provided the only easy outlet to the Mediterranean: entering the mouth of the little Cyrus River, the boats could climb to its head of navigation; there a portage over a low watershed would bring them to the Phasis River, down which there was a clear run to the Black Sea and on through the Dardanelles towards Greece and Italy.

During the third and second centuries B.C., serious attempts to develop the southern sea route were made by the Seleucids' chief rivals, the Greek Ptolemies who ruled in Egypt. Little was known of the shape and extent of the Arabian peninsula, and nothing of the ocean beyond the Gulf of Aden, except that Scylax had crossed it and that Arab and Indian traders were regularly exchanging products. Nevertheless, Ptolemy II (285–246 B.C.) set about energetically to make the Red Sea an Egyptian lake. He improved existing ports along its shores and built new ones, linking them by good caravan roads with the Nile, and thence by boat with his capital, the great new market city of Alexandria. Remembering the dreams of Necho and Darius, he opened a canal connecting a branch of the lower Nile with the Gulf of Suez. This triumphant accomplishment turned out to be somewhat disappointing, however, because uncertain winds and other navigational difficulties in the northern parts of the Red Sea made it hazardous for sailing boats to enter the Suez gulf. Ptolemy's sailors actually used much more the ports farther south along the coast.

Nevertheless, his canal remained as a symbol of east-west communication strong enough to attract the Romans to the conquest of his country two centuries later. When the final chapter of Egypt's defeat was written, and Cleopatra fled back from the Battle of Actium, some say that she was trying to get her ships into the canal she had lost and away to some hiding place in India; if the Nile had not been too low at the time to admit her vessels, she might have escaped both Augustus and the viper. Be that as it may, the canal and its possibilities continued to tempt the Romans. Trajan (d. A.D. 117), when he was making his futile bid to reconstitute Alexander's empire under his own rule, renovated the old canal in the hope that it might provide a major line of communication. After his failure, the waterway fell into disrepair again and was finally abandoned. But the memory of a man-made river on which one might sail across the desert in one lap of a continuous voyage from Europe to the Orient remained to fascinate hundreds of engineers and empire builders all down the centuries to Napoleon and de Lesseps and Disraeli.

The second Ptolemy found that if he could get his ships to Aden he could buy Indian imports from the Arabs for considerably less than he would have to pay his Seleucid rivals to deliver them to Syrian ports. For over a century, the Egyptians remained content to deal with Arab middlemen. But towards the end of the second century B.C., when some wild nomads called Parthians had driven out the Seleucids and were holding the Euphrates route even more tightly than their predecessors, an Indian sailor, the sole survivor of a shipwreck in the Gulf of Aden, turned up in Alexandria. As the price of repatriation, he offered to guide an Egyptian ship to India. This time the ruling Ptolemy decided to attempt to break the monopoly of the Arab middlemen. A Greek nautical captain in his fleet, one Eudoxus of Cyzicus, undertook to get the Indian home. He succeeded, returned with a valuable cargo, and subsequently made several more voyages, on one of them going down the coast of Africa and discovering the sources of other articles which the Arabs had been offering to Egyptian traders.

It may be that the Indian sailor was able to get passage home because he tempted his captors with a prize they could not resist. For at just about this time, a new article began to come into the international market, one that was destined for a time to stimulate the craving of importers even more than pepper. From some mysterious source in the unknown east, Indian traders began to bring a lustrous, shimmering textile whose beauty took men's breath. Silk was a wonder such as men in the Mediterranean world had never seen nor imagined, and it quickly became a thing desired above rubies.

Yet strangely enough, the Ptolemies never really developed the direct importation which Eudoxus had made possible. Some think the later members of the dynasty were too weak and lazy to contest seriously with the Arabs, and that since all foreign trade was a royal monopoly, private sailors and traders were discouraged from taking the necessary risks on their own account. But a more probable reason was the emergence onto the world stage of yet another vast empire with another rich and exotic civilization. China, where the silk originated, had recently achieved her own imperial stage of development and was reaching towards a direct contact with the "barbarians," as she supposed them, who lived beyond the realm of the "emperor of all under heaven." And her efforts led, at first, away from India.

One of the early, and formidable, emperors of the great Han dynasty, Wu Ti, discovered around 128 B.C. that some of his former subjects at the western end of the Great Wall had been driven away into the unknown by nomadic raiders. He dispatched one of his generals, Chang Ch'ien, to search for them and at the same time to examine the condition of the trade routes over which there had already been some contact with India. To find the missing subjects, Chang Ch'ien traveled westward along already known routes to the lake in central Sinkiang where the Tarim River ends. There the road divided, one branch proceeding up the Tarim to Kashgar, where it was rejoined by the other, which had swung south and west along a line of oases watered by streams flowing down from the Kunlun Mountains. Indian colonists, incidentally, were already established in these oases, forwarding goods along from one to the next. By one route or the other, Chang Ch'ien reached Kashgar, where the road mainly used at that time went south, over "headache mountains" and "hanging passes," to Gilgit on the Indus and thence down into India. The Chinese general, however, seems to have taken an even more difficult trail that went westward from Kashgar into the land that had been called Bactria, between the Jaxartes and Oxus rivers.

When he finally returned to China, Chang Ch'ien took with him from Bactria the seeds of the grape, which thus became one of the West's first and most delectable gifts to the Orient. He also brought the news that the missing Chinese subjects had been pushed down into the Kabul Valley, where they were to remain for a few centuries as rulers of a kingdom called Kushan and as another troublesome middleman who could, and often did, seize control of the Indus trade route. But the most exciting news he brought was that the land west of Kashgar, all the way to distant western seas, was now in the hands of the Parthians, and that these people were eager for trade. Envoys were promptly sent out, and they reached the court of Mithridates II about 115 B.C. Presumably a satisfactory trade treaty was arranged, for during the years from 114 to 108, according to Chinese annals, ten large caravans a year were reaching Ferghana. The Parthians, able to buy directly from the Chinese and ship either by the Caspian route or across Iran and Mesopotamia to the Syrian coast, seem to have been able to undercut the Ptolemies, who had at best to deal with Indian middlemen. It was silk Parthian flags that first startled and fascinated Mediterranean observers, half a century before Cleopatra's silken dresses became the envy and despair of Roman matrons.

All men were dazzled by silk, but those who were most affected with a burning greed to possess it were the otherwise sober citizens of the new state that had risen to power far out in the western fringes of civilization. The glint and feel of the royal textile seems to have intoxicated the Romans, whose bodies had known no gentler cloth than homespun and linsey-woolsey. The traditional Roman toga was made of wool, scratchy and hot in an Italian summer, and harsh linen underclothing did little to make the heavy robes more comfortable. But the cotton of India and the silk of China were such stuffs as dreams are made on, dreams of luxury so seductive that they could rouse a Roman general to his greatest exertions. As gold had lured Darius, so it seems that in Roman senators the rustle of silk stirred a greed for possession matched in later history only by the Dutch passion for tulips in the seventeenth century.

During the last century before Christ, the Romans, having taken over most of the kingdoms that had once paid tribute to Macedonia, tried again and again to establish themselves in Asia Minor and the Caucasus, apparently seeking a northern route to the silk land. Beaten off by the Parthians, they turned their attention to the Syrian coast, where goods arrived both from the Euphrates route and from a caravan road that came up from South Arabia through Petra into Palestine. Here they were more successful, though they still had to deal with Parthian and Arabian middlemen. With the conquest of Egypt, however, they won control of the Red Sea, and only the Arabs stood between them and the markets of India.

They were able to break these competitors because of the superiority of their ships and the daring of a Greek navigator named Hippalus. Arab dhows were sewn together with coconut fiber, and were not very seaworthy in rough water; they had therefore usually kept close to the coasts in getting around to Indian ports and had not ventured out into the Indian Ocean during the time when the southwest monsoon was blowing. Hippalus, however, having large wooden ships held together with nails, decided to risk sailing directly across the ocean from Aden to the Indian coast, with the high wind at his back. It was a rough and dangerous voyage, but a far faster one than the Arabs could make. Roman traders followed his route and beat out the Arabs by the simple trick of getting there first with the most.

Thus "India was brought near for gain," as Pliny remarked. And here again, a number of local rivers came into the collective consciousness, for they provided the keys to the development of trade across the subcontinent. Foreign traders bring to any river a different set of attitudes from those of the people who live along its banks: they are not interested in its irrigation possibilities, for example; what they want to know is whether it is navigable, or whether its valley can carry an overland trade route from a source of supply to a market. When they ventured into unknown territory, they kept as close to the rivers as paleolithic hunters had done, and for the same reasons. Fresh drinking water is a daily necessity, and a flowing stream is the safest guide. That is why the caravans across Sinkiang generally preferred to follow the Tarim River, and why in Central Asia the most important landmark was the Oxus. For the Romans, the rivers of India assumed the same kind of importance.

There was first the well-known Indus, in whose delta ocean-going vessels could load silk and furs that had come down from Central Asia. But farther south along the coast they could reach the mouths of hitherto unsuspected rivers like the Narbada; from there a route went upstream to a portage that led over into the Ganges Valley, and along it moved a stream of traffic bringing cotton goods and jewels and "the reed honey called sacchari" (cane sugar). Greek and Roman ships in the spice trade went straight across the Indian Ocean to reach ports on the Malabar coast in the south. From these, again, there were usable rivers and portages (the Cauvery was the major waterway) that led directly to the east coast. It was not long before Roman traders were pushing up that coast to the mouths of the Ganges and Brahmaputra, and even perhaps to the golden ports of Burma, always seeking a direct route to the land of the silkworm.

Second only to silk as an article of value was pepper. Once the Romans got hold of a route to India and the trade was established, large Pepper Barns were built beside the Tiber, and keeping them filled became one of the major objectives of Roman policy. The inveterate gossip, Pliny, writing in the first century A.D., professed astonishment that

> pepper has come so much into fashion, seeing that it . . . has nothing in it that can plead as a recommendation to either fruit or berry, its only desirable quality being a certain pungency; and yet it is for this that we import it all the way from India! Who was the first to make trial of it as an article of food? And who, I wonder,

was the man that was not content to prepare himself, by hunger only, for the satisfaction of a greedy appetite? (Quoted by Wheeler: *Rome Beyond the Imperial Frontiers,* p. 148.)

Nevertheless, greedy appetites have played their part in shaping the course of history, and for over fifteen hundred years the craving for pepper was to remain a driving force in empire building.

About the time that Pliny wrote, attention was again shifted momentarily to the possibilities of a northern route that would by-pass both the Parthians and the Indians. Border troubles in the Parthian districts of Central Asia had long since disrupted the trade Mithridates and Wu Ti had set up, and nomads from the north had wrested Sinkiang from Chinese control. But in the years between A.D. 73 and 91, the brilliant general Pan Ch'ao reconquered for his emperor the whole territory traversed by the Silk Roads clear to Ferghana. There he exchanged envoys with the Parthians, and once again, as the Chinese annalists record with evident satisfaction, "foreign traders knocked daily at the Barriers." Apparently the Parthians began to use again the Caspian-Caucasus route for shipping the silk along to the Roman market, for one of their subject peoples living along it, when they plotted rebellion, sent envoys to Nero to solicit his aid, doubtless with the promise of giving him, in return, access to a silk route where he would have to pay no Parthian tolls. Although it is another curious example of how those two minor streams, the Cyrus and the Phasis, keep popping in and out of Roman history, nothing definite seems to have come of this scheme. Nero was absorbed at the time in trying to prove that he was the greatest actor in the world, and his interest in silk seems

168

PLATE 11. *The wide arch of empire.* The Roman aqueduct near Tarragona. (Photograph by courtesy of the Spanish Dirección General del Turismo)

PLATE 12. *Interior of a Byzantine cistern*, "like a vast drowned cathedral." The great reservoir known as Yerebatan Sarayi, built in Istanbul by the Byzantine emperors, and still in use. (Photograph by courtesy of the National Tourist Office of Turkey)

PLATE 13. *The river as teacher of geography.* A strip from the bronze gate on the palace at Balawat, showing Shalmaneser's discovery of the source of the Tigris, 852 B.C. In the lower right-hand part of the section shown here, the river is flowing out of a mountain (represented by the conventional "scale pattern"). In order to show men who have waded into the cave to explore it, with firebrands to give them light, the artist has pretended that three "windows" are cut in the side of the mountain. At the extreme right, a soldier stands guard on the cliff outside. At the entrance to the natural tunnel, a sculptor has set a large rock in the stream so that he can reach a place high on the rocky wall to carve a "mighty image of [Shalmaneser's] majesty." A helper seems to be handing tools up to him from the bank, and farther downstream men are leading a ram and a bull for sacrifice. In the upper panel, the king has arrived at a grotto where water drips from the ceiling onto stalagmites, probably the ultimate source of the stream. He is inspecting the work of another sculptor who seems to be chiseling an inscription on the cave wall (doubtless the one which recorded "the glory of Assur my lord, my deeds of valor, all that I had accomplished in the lands"). Frankfort describes the rest of the scene: "In front of the grotto a bull is slaughtered. On the mountain is a castle or fortified settlement; to the right appears, it seems, a native amazed at the intrusion. But on the left we catch a glimpse of the Assyrian army, leaving this scene with its purposeful stride, bound for further exploits." (Photograph by courtesy of the British Museum)

PLATE 14. *The water wheels at Hama, on the Orontes River in Syria.*
The most famous existing examples of the *noria*, the earliest machine in
which water power was used to perform work. The larger of the wheels
shown here is some seventy feet in diameter. The aqueduct which
receives the water from the top of the wheel and carries it away to irrigate the fields is of Roman construction. (Photograph by courtesy of the
Syrian Ministry for Foreign Affairs)

PLATE 15. *The wheel at the cistern.* A Mogul painting of the early seventeenth century showing the type of water-lifting device commonly used in India. It is like the Egyptian *saqiyah*, animal-powered and geared. The vertical wheel, only the top of which is shown in this painting, normally turns an axle on the other end of which is attached either a pot-hung wheel or the upper pulley that carries a chain-of-buckets, depending on the depth of the well. (Photograph by courtesy of the British Museum)

PLATE 16. *The idea of a multipurpose structure.* A view of the great barrage over the Karun River at Shushtar, which carries a roadway on its top. The lower parts of the present structure were built by Shapur I shortly after 260 A.D. (including the sluice gates for controlling the flow of the river). The upper parts date from the early Islamic and Seljuk periods. The whole structure of dam and bridge is a good example of the way the Arabs adopted the water-controlling techniques of their predecessors, preserving, repairing, and extending earlier structures. (Photograph by courtesy of Hunting Aerosurveys Ltd.)

PLATE 17. *A Moslem "earthly paradise."* Mosaic from the courtyard cloister of the Great Mosque in Damascus, showing the city of Damascus in the center on the banks of the Barada River, and at either side villages in the Ghutah, with trees indicating that the land is irrigated. (Photograph by courtesy of the Syrian Ministry for Foreign Affairs)

PLATE 18. *The food of the riverine cities.* A clay toy (fifth century B.C., probably from Tanagra) representing a mule carrying a single enormous fish, very much like the *biz* which was the principal food of Baghdad fifteen hundred years later. The fact that this object was designed as a child's plaything suggests that it was a common sight in ancient traffic. (Photograph by courtesy of the British Museum)

PLATE 19. *Carnival on the river*. The Dragon Boat Procession, one of the great river festivals of ancient China, which was held every year on the fifth day of the fifth month. It commemorated the poet and statesman, Ch'u Yuan, who drowned himself in the Mi-lo River in 295 B.C. In this eighteenth-century tapestry panel, the decorated barges are shown engaged in the traditional search for the body of the poet, while people on the banks of the river prepare rice to be thrown into the river in order to propitiate his spirit. (Photograph by kind permission of the Victoria and Albert Museum, London)

to have been confined to designing costumes that would set off his genius most dazzlingly.

In any event, during the following century the bulk of Roman imports still came from India; in fact, the monsoon trade was greater than ever. The Parthians, in an effort to minimize it, opened some of their overland routes to foreign traders, hoping to make up in taxes what they were losing in direct profit. The geographer Ptolemy, writing about the middle of the second century, tells how a trader named Maes Titianus sent his agents regularly across Syria and the Parthian lands to Bactria; it is certain that he paid heavy transit tolls for the privilege.

The constant uncertainty of all the overland routes to China, which were apt to be cut at any time by the continual warfare of the small border kingdoms and the raids of restless nomads, prompted both the Romans and the Indians of the Ganges to search for a sea route which would be safe. India at the time was entering her great cultural-imperial age, during which, for a thousand years, her civilization, though not her rule, would be dominant over all of Southeast Asia; and Rome was at the height of her expansion. Both were prepared to reach as far as they could. So long as they could trade profitably with each other, they seem to have been willing to "coexist," each having a sufficiently large field for its exploits far away from the other's precincts. Oddly enough, the trade was all in India's favor. Having little to exchange that the Indians wanted, Rome was forced to pay in precious metals. But greed for luxuries drove her to drain her resources willingly, and gold flowed into Indian coffers as it had once flowed into the treasury of Darius. The arrangement seems to have satisfied both parties. But they were nevertheless rivals in the attempt to tap the silk market at its source.

The Indians reached it first; after circling clear around

the Malay peninsula, their envoys made harbor in the Red River delta in Tongking in A.D. 159, and returned again two years later. But the Romans were on their heels, for in 166 the Chinese annalists record that "after Ta-ts'in [Rome] had long been hindered from intercourse by the An-si [Parthians] between, its king An-tun [Marcus Aurelius Antoninus] sent envoys; they came [by sea] to the Tongking frontier." In the following century they were back again, visits being recorded in 226 and 284. The Chinese, in the meantime, had once again lost control of the Tarim River branch of the Great Silk Road, and Indian colonists were abandoning their trading posts on the southern branch across Sinkiang because a phase of climatic desiccation was drying up the oases. At the same time, quarrelsome local rulers were once again disrupting the flow of traffic on the old Kashgar-Indus valley road, and this also made the Indians look seaward.

It seemed as if everything was conspiring to open one of the great ages of ocean navigation, and that the four imperial powers—Rome, China, Persia, and India—would inevitably be drawn into a kind of world trading community in which seafaring ships would provide the means of communication and international exchange of goods and ideas among four high civilizations. Ships might sail, it seemed, from ports in the steamy deltas of Irrawaddy or Brahmaputra, to deliver their strange cargoes on the wharves of Ctesiphon on the Euphrates. Conversely, from Massilia on the Rhone and Ostia on the Tiber, vessels might converge upon the canal Trajan had renovated, whence the tin and the cheap Samian tableware and above all, the gold, might be carried on to be distributed in the valleys of the Narbada or the Ganges, or even sent up the Red River to come to rest finally in some pavilion overlooking the muddy Hwang Ho. More importantly, perhaps, over such a system of communications Greek mathematicians and Roman engineers, Indian artists, Chinese hydraulic experts, Persian astronomers, Egyptian craftsmen, and Jewish sages might have traveled freely, and from the cross fertilization of culture with culture men might have achieved a community of interests in which all could have some productive share.

There are several reasons why such a world community was not built in the third and fourth centuries of the Christian era. In China, which had been a unified empire for four hundred years, the Han dynasty crumbled, and the empire was divided in A.D. 220 among three kingdoms which spent the next half century in fruitless warfare with one another. The three Warring Kingdoms were followed by two, and China was not unified again until the seventh century. At almost exactly the same time, the Parthian rulers were driven out of Persia by a line of local princes called Sassanids. Strong and vigorous in managing domestic affairs, the Sassanids were not internationalists and had no interest in co-operating with the hated Romans; on the contrary, they renewed the ancient quarrel with redoubled force, and for the next four hundred years bled their own people and those of the enemy in a struggle which accomplished nothing but the eventual destruction of both empires. Rome, herself, in the third century had already passed her zenith. Hounded by the barbarians along all her European frontiers, confronted with a revitalized enemy in Asia, and with an economic situation at home that grew worse each year, she was forced to retract the long arm that had reached out greedily towards the Orient. By the mid-fourth century, affairs in the Imperial City had become so bad that even the emperors no longer wanted to live in it any more than necessary. A second capital was established in A.D. 330 at Constantinople (Byzantium) and by the end of the century the dying western limbs of the empire were amputated and thrown to barbarian "emperors." All that was left of Roman grandeur was concentrated thereafter on Byzantium. The various kingdoms of India, in the meantime, were reunited about A.D. 320 under a brilliant dynasty known as the Guptas. Most of these rulers were very able men, but like the Sassanids in Persia they showed little interest in east-west contacts. They withdrew almost completely from the monsoon trade, allowing it to be taken over again by Arab middlemen. The explanation seems to be that the disintegration of Rome made this trade far less valuable and that the Guptas preferred to concentrate on Southeast Asia where they had thriving colonies and trading posts and a free hand in dealing with them.

The last four centuries of the classical imperial age (roughly from 225 to 640) saw a general and continuing decline in international intercourse. The idea of a world community receded steadily into the background, as men made fewer and fewer efforts in any of the activities that might have fostered it. There were, of course, some contacts, and occasional attempts to re-establish connections. For example, a whole succession of Buddhist pilgrims, starting with Fa-Hien in A.D. 339, made the arduous journey overland from China to visit shrines in India, and these pilgrims undoubtedly helped to preserve communication between the two great Oriental civilizations. The Sassanids made some efforts to reopen the Central Asian routes, and we hear of several embassies passing that way between Persia and China. There was even some use of the sea routes which Indians and Romans had opened, for there are fourth-century records of Chinese ships in the Euphrates.

But the great customer in the west, who had baited with gold the long lines flung out eastward and had drawn them back heavy with pepper and silk, was no longer in the market. There were occasional flurries of activity, when Byzantine rulers felt momentarily rich enough or strong enough to venture. Justinian, for example, tried to use the Red Sea route again, encouraging the Christian kingdoms near its mouth to bring him silk from India because silk workers in his Syrian territories were having difficulty in meeting Persian prices. They reported back that the supply there had been bought up by Persians. Justinian announced a price above which he would not pay, but the Persians, having a corner on the market, refused to meet it, and the Syrian workers were ruined. At length the emperor resorted to espionage; he employed either "some monks" or "a certain Persian" (there are two versions of the story) to slip through the Persian lands to some place where silk was produced and smuggle out some silkworm eggs. The coveted eggs reached Constantinople around A.D. 552, and from that time onward caterpillars were fed on Greek mulberry leaves and silk was unwound and spun on Byzantine territory. The industry expanded too slowly, however, to meet the demand: some twenty years later Byzantine envoys were again working their way painfully across Central Asia to the tent of a "great Khan" who was said to possess silk, in an effort to reopen the old Caspian-Black Sea route.

On the whole, however, international communication was dying, as the classical empires who had almost achieved it lost their grip and turned inward on themselves. The decline persisted and deepened until the coming of the Arabs and a reunified China in the seventh century. Rivers that had come for a moment into the notice of men from one end of the known world to the other sank back into the obscurity of local streams, their wharves no more crowded with curious people come to stare at some outlandish craft from a distant land. The emperors had striven mightily, and, as we shall see, they had given rivers in general much increased significance in the lives of men. But it was not within their capacity to make them the sinews of a world community. It is said that Trajan, standing on the shores of the Persian Gulf at that moment when he knew he had reached the limit of his exertions, wept as he watched a ship setting forth on the long voyage to India.

CHAPTER VII

The Wide Arch of Empire

NEAR the middle of the fourth century A.D., the Sassanid Shapur II was trying to drive the Romans out of a series of towns they had fortified in Syria. Around one of these, a place called Nisibis, the Romans had built a triple fortification so high that Shapur's soldiers, if they came under the walls, were perfect targets for a downpour of boiling oil. But near the city was a little river called the Jaghjagh, and Shapur knew from the experience of many earlier generals that a river could be made into a weapon.

At a safe distance back from the walls, he built an earthen dike encircling the town; then, into the space between, he diverted the Jaghjagh. Before long, Nisibis was sitting in the middle of a lake, and on that lake Shapur proceeded to launch a fleet. Siege engines, mounted on rafts, brought his troops up to the walls, where they could fight almost on a level with the defenders. Again and again the Romans beat them off, but at length the river did what the Persians could not do: the pressure of the mounting water broke the walls, and through a great breach the lake suddenly began to pour into the town. Into the madly swirling torrent Shapur threw a column of heavily armed cavalry and a troop of elephants, wild with fear and bellowing as they floundered against Roman spears. Sucked into the rushing current, rafts were swept through the breach into the city, their siege ladders toppling against houses and flinging the archers into the welter of animals and men who were struggling for footing in the flood.

Everybody, attackers and defenders alike, seems to have fought as well as men could fight in such a melee, but at nightfall both armies were in such general havoc that no one could tell who were victors and who vanquished. The commanders agreed to a truce, Shapur withdrew the remnant of his forces and the next day took them off to fight against a barbarian invasion on his eastern borders, while the citizens of Nisibis set about the dreary task of cleaning up the mess.

Such was the scale on which the emperors did things, and one sees it in all their military operations. Warfare was still the order of the day. All the classical empires, though they were essentially devices for organizing international trade and skimming off the cream of the profits through tax collection, were military states, created and controlled by naked force. For this reason, the movements of troops, the supply of garrisons, the sudden seizure of outlying districts, or the suppression of revolt in long-conquered regions were just as insistent problems to the successors of Alexander and the Roman governors as they had been to Sargon. Their solutions differed from his only in the scale of their operations and the relative size of their armies, their equipment, and their military structures. When they used rivers, they used them as Hollywood di-

176

rectors might, and they sometimes achieved effects that would be the envy of those whose ambition is to achieve the colossal.

Throughout the thousand years from Darius (d. 486 B.C.) to Justinian (d. A.D. 565), for example, military strategists and tacticians were able to think of no new way to move an army across a river. But they made prodigious accomplishments in mere size. Where earlier kings had marched thousands of men, the emperors sent hundreds of thousands. If Herodotus is to be believed, the land and naval forces Xerxes brought against Greece totaled over five million men, and "as for eunuchs, female cooks, and soldiers' women, no one could attempt an estimate of their number, any more than of the various pack-animals and Indian dogs which followed the army." Though the army was probably smaller than Herodotus estimated, it was certainly large enough to pose some very serious problems to its leaders whenever a river lay in its path.

All the older methods of crossing—fording, the use of floats and rafts, and even Croesus' trick of diversion—were practiced at one time or another by the commanders of such hordes. But in the imperial ages there seems to have been a great deal more building of temporary bridges than in earlier times. The best-known of such bridges was one of the smallest: the wooden structure Caesar threw across a small stream in Gaul, of which generations of second-year Latin students have made scale models. Five hundred years later, the Emperor Jovian's engineers built over the Tigris an immense floating bridge supported by inflated animal skins. The bridge broke in the swift current, and the soldiers had to cross the river individually as best they could. But such bridges, even when they stood up, were quick makeshifts compared with the gigantic structures over which Darius, at the very beginning of the imperial ages, crossed the Danube and the straits of the Bosphorus, or the great double bridge over the Hellespont whose destruction roused the ire of Xerxes. Frustrated by the storm, the furious monarch had not only lashed the sea, but even went so far as to behead the Phoenician and Egyptian engineers who had built the two bridges. When he finally calmed down, however, he realized that his army was still on the Asian shore.

What followed gives us a good insight into the way things were done in the grandiose days of the "King in this great earth far and wide." Xerxes gave orders, and immediately two new bridges were begun. All the galleys and triremes in the fleet were drawn up side by side in two files stretching from shore to shore—360 vessels in one and 314 in the other—and tightly anchored with their prows pointing upstream. Then thick cables, two of papyrus and four of flax for each bridge, were stretched across these ship pontoons and pulled taut by winches on the shores. A solid plank floor was laid on the cables, covered with brushwood and a layer of earth packed down hard. When palings had been built along the edges to prevent the horses from seeing the water and leaping off in fear, the king was told that the bridges were ready for his use. The army prepared to move, and this time a sobered Xerxes conducted himself in the approved manner.

> . . . while they waited for the sun which they wished to see as it rose, they burned all sorts of spices on the bridges and laid myrtle boughs along the way. Then sunrise came, and Xerxes poured wine into the sea out of a golden goblet and, with his face turned to the sun, prayed that no chance might prevent him from conquering Europe or turn him back before he reached its utmost limits. His prayer ended, he flung the cup into the

Hellespont and with it a golden bowl and a Persian *acinaces,* or short sword. I cannot say for certain if he intended the things which he threw into the water to be an offering to the Sun-god; perhaps they were—or it may be that they were a gift to the Hellespont itself, to show he was sorry for having caused it to be lashed with whips. (Herodotus, Bk. VII, p. 436.)

Then the great army began to cross, the infantry and cavalry by the upper bridge and the pack animals and all the noncombatants by the lower one. The omens were terrifying: first there was an eclipse; then a mare gave birth to a rabbit; and finally a story came up the lines of sweating men that back in Sardis a mule had foaled, and as if the mere event were not horrible enough, the unnatural offspring had been a monster with both male and female sexual organs. But the bridges held together under those millions of marching steps, and for seven days and nights without a break the men, women, and animals poured across into Greece, while "from the European shore, Xerxes watched his troops coming over under the whips."

There are two details here that go far to explain why, in the new order of things, such colossal undertakings could be carried out. One is the mention of Egyptian and Phoenician engineers. The other is that sinister remark about whips.

The imperial age marks the advent into history of the professional engineer. In building records from earlier times we are often told the name of the king who ordered the construction of a tunnel, an aqueduct, or a public monument. Since the kings were too busy to do personally all that is credited to them, even if they had been expert in a dozen crafts besides that of kingship, we know that they must have depended on commoners. Hammurabi

179

did not design the irrigation systems he administered; Sennacherib must have been served by some brilliant Assyrian engineers; at the courts of the Pharaohs there were undoubtedly many Egyptians of genius. But the names of the master builders of antiquity are unrecorded and unknown. With the coming of vast empires, however, and the payment of fees in gold, the engineer begins to emerge as a person in his own right, a highly skilled professional whose services win him honor and wealth, and the more satisfying reward of a permanent reputation.

We do not know the names of the engineers who built the bridges for Xerxes, though their nationality is perhaps a piece of more important information. It is characteristic of the first "world" empire that they were not Persians, but cosmopolitans, like the artisans who worked on Darius' palace, chosen for their job because they were expert at it. Brains, like turquoise and yaka wood and gold, could now be drawn easily from whatever mine offered the richest ore. In the service of the emperors, a man of any nationality could find the opportunity to make the most of his talents.

Phoenicians and Egyptians were generally regarded as the peoples with the highest engineering skill. But the earliest engineers whose names have come down to us were a group who lived on the Greek island of Samos in the sixth century B.C.: Eupalinus who built the aqueduct there, Rhoecus whose masterpiece was the largest Greek temple in existence, and Mandrocles who bridged the Bosphorus for the army of Darius. From the time these men flourished, engineering in all its many forms becomes a recognized profession and its practitioners, indispensable to imperial greatness, are identifiable persons. The roll call that begins with the Samian builders continues through the large group who accompanied Alexander on all his conquests

(336–323 B.C.) and doubtless contributed much to their success: Gorgos the Metal-Worker, who knew the art of boring wells and must have been the most important man in the army on its long desert marches; Diades of Thessaly, who was expert in making siege machines; Nearchus and Onesicrates, nautical experts who could probably build anything from a raft to a fleet. Whenever he paused to found one of the numerous towns he called Alexandria, the young conqueror must have relied heavily on the advice of men like Bacton, Diognetos, and Philonides, all of whom were geographers and surveyors; Deinocrates, the town planner; and above all Aristobulos, the famous architect and engineer. Before long, the scientists began to write books, and from the Hellenistic period down through the long stretch of the Roman and Byzantine empires, they were able to record their accomplishments themselves. It is no accident that the name of Vitruvius is better known than those of most Roman emperors.

The structure of the empires made such a development inevitable. Talented men could move freely about the world, unrestricted by language or religion or nationality, offering their services to the highest bidder. With much of known mankind co-operating to pay their expenses, the emperors could authorize construction on whatever grandiose scale an engineer might dream, and usually the larger it was the more eager was the emperor to see it completed. No river was too wide to bridge, no spring too far away in the hills to be brought down through immense tunnels and over incredibly high structures to play in a courtyard fountain.

There was also that matter of the whips. For the imperial engineer, there was never any question of finding the labor to carry out his plans; the empires were built on slave labor, and whether the worker was actually sold into slavery or sold himself as a mercenary soldier, the whip was never far from his back. There was literally no limit to what he could do because only death could end his struggle to do it, and the death of a slave was nothing because there were hundreds of others to take his place. Through the whole period, down to the economic upheaval of the fourth century A.D. when Rome was reeling under the blows of the barbarians, there was a continuing and enormous surplus of labor, under the control of completely ruthless force.

Slavery was basic in the economies of India and China, as well as in the western countries. Agriculture, however, seems to have been carried on mostly by people whose status was more like that of the feudal serf, tied to the land and owing for the privilege a host of dues and services to the overlords. The great waterworks in the Oriental countries were built largely with forced labor which the peasants were obliged to perform as a condition of being allowed to till the soil. Since there was no other way in which they could live, they had no more choice in the matter than the slaves.

There was plenty for engineers and slaves to do in the ancient empires. No matter how briskly trade might flourish, nor how successfully the generals might harry the outlands, the basic needs of most people were still to eat and to drink. Agriculture remained the foundation of all human activity, and, since the bulk of the population and of the cultivated land in the west was in the arid belt, irrigation and water supply were still daily and pressing concerns. The one annual downpour in India, and the combination of floods and porous soil in China, placed agriculture in those countries under the same compulsions.

To meet these needs, the emperors used many of the traditional devices for diverting and controlling rivers. But because the imperial realms had spread far beyond the basin of a single great river, and included lands where there were no usable surface rivers at all, they were obliged to build a variety of structures that could make use of other water sources. Caravan stops, garrisons, seaports, and market cities tend to grow up at strategic points, rather than at places ideally suited by nature for human settlement. In order to supply them, the imperial engineers worked with great ingenuity. In the massive waterworks of the period that extends roughly from 500 B.C. to A.D. 500, there is sometimes less emphasis on using large rivers than on getting along without them.

In order to control and make the most of whatever water resources they had, each of the great empires seems to have concentrated on some particular type of structure. Ancient Egypt had produced the ditch and had built around it her system of basin irrigation; in the valley of the Twin Rivers, the need for perennial irrigation and flood control had made the dam the essential structure; and in the cities of the old Indus civilization the most noticeable feature was the plumbing system and the baths. In the same way, each of the later empires had its distinctive type of water engineering.

The Persians, living in hilly country where rivers were few and far between, concentrated on the *qanat,* an underground river artificially created by digging a nearly horizontal tunnel from the plain back into the bowels of a hill and tapping a deep artesian source. The *qanat* may be a Persian invention, though as we have noted there is a possibility that the technique was known to Sennacherib and was used at Erbil. But whether they invented it or not, they have used it more consistently than any other people, and have fixed it in the world's mind as a thoroughly Persian thing. The Achaemenians built *qanats* all over the Iranian plateau and beyond, and from there the technique radiated far and wide. It is a technique that testifies, incidentally, to a high development of engineering skill. To drive a tunnel in a straight line and keep its bed steadily but very gradually rising towards the level of a stream that is hidden miles away under a high hill is no mean accomplishment. The mind plans and the hands make what the eye cannot see, and water is brought from the darkness under the earth into sunlight. The *qanat* is a great step in men's exploration of the unknown.

All over Iran today the *qanat* is the standard source, many of them extending as much as twenty miles. Villages grow up along the courses, for the hidden stream can be tapped all the way along by wells dug down from the surface, as many as a thousand such wells being supplied by the larger ones. The man-made underground river is the sole source of water for millions of people not only in Iran, but through the Middle East and up into Central Asia as far as Sinkiang; there are even a few in China proper. *Qanats* have been found in Oman on the southeast coast of Arabia, where the terrain is very like that of the Persian plateau, and Darius is said to have dug one to supply the oasis of Kharga in Egypt. When the Arabs reached their period of expansion over a thousand years later, they carried the technique into North Africa. Modern desert scientists, struggling to reclaim some parts of the arid lands, have adopted the device and are in many places finding it an essential tool: at Béni-Abbès in Algeria, for example, the gardens of the Institute of Saharan Research are watered by an ancient *qanat*, discovered and renovated by the French scientists at the station, which draws water from deep under the mountainous sand dunes.

There is very little contemporary information about waterworks in ancient India, but what there is indicates that there, also, a characteristic structure was developed, and this is confirmed by modern archaeology. Tank irrigation, as it is called, was the Indian solution to the problems of alternating flood and drought posed by the fact that the subcontinent has only one rainfall in each year. Most of the year, the skies are cloudless and the land is dry. In the valleys of the great rivers, of course, water can be taken off in canals just as it is done in Mesopotamia, although towards the end of the dry season the rivers are likely to become perilously low. In the hilly country of the south and west, however, the torrential downpours brought by the monsoon drain off in floods and leave only drought behind them. The great task of the Indian farmer is to catch and store up enough of this runoff to carry his family and his beasts and his fields through until the rains come again. His means is the tank or reservoir, sometimes a lake in the hills made by stopping a gorge with a dam, and sometimes a large pond excavated on gently sloping land and protected all round with a high dike. By holding back some of the rainfall, tanks help to minimize flood damage during the monsoon period; then through the long dry spell the water can be let out gradually for domestic supplies and for irrigation.

These devices were well-established in Indian usage by the time Chandragupta created the first unified empire. Megasthenes noticed the prime importance that was attached to irrigation generally, and reported that the emperor maintained in his government a special Irrigation Department, whose officers were charged with measuring the lands for the purpose of calculating the water tax, and regulating the sluices so that all farmers got their fair share of water from the canals. A thousand miles away from the capital city, one of his provincial governors created the first "tank" of which we have record, though its successful building in a remote corner of the empire suggests that the technique was thoroughly familiar and had long been practiced. At Girnar near the Arabian Sea, he made Lake Sudarsana ("the beautiful") by damming up a small stream, and began to use it for irrigation. Supplementary channels were built during the reign of Chandragupta's grandson, Asoka (273–232 B.C.), and the system functioned until an exceptionally violent storm in A.D. 150 broke the dam and the lake flowed away. The provincial satrap at the time was a man named Rudradaman, and we know his name and all the early history of Sudarsana because he not only rebuilt the dam "three times stronger," but proudly recorded his achievement in an inscription cut into solid rock on the hill above. Rudradaman's work lasted three hundred years; the dam did not burst again until A.D. 458. This time the powerful Guptas were ruling a reunified empire, and the emperor lost no time in commanding his local governor to repair the damage. It was only long afterwards, when India was again in a period of confusion and decay, that the dam was allowed to fall into ruin and the beautiful lake eventually disappeared, after having served the people of Girnar almost a thousand years.

The technique of tank irrigation was practiced all over southern India, and is still today the most effective means of storing the monsoon rains. From India it spread into Ceylon, where it was introduced by conquerors from the mainland and where for a thousand years it remained the basic factor in the wealth and power of that kingdom. During recent centuries, tank irrigation was neglected and an enormous part of the island became a "dry zone," uncultivated and uninhabited, because the interests of those in authority was concentrated on the tea plantations in the well-watered hills. But today the government of Ceylon is attempting to revive the ancient practice on a grand scale, pinning much of its hope for future development on the resettlement in the "dry zone" of some of its heavily concentrated population.

In all the ancient empires, water conservancy and river use had in general the same objectives. The difference between the practices of one people and those of another are differences in the means by which they try to reach those objectives. These are brought about by differences in land and climate, in the natures of the particular rivers involved, and of course by differences among the civilizations themselves. All primitive peoples seem to go through very much the same steps in gradually learning to use and control their rivers, and all seem to take a given step at the same stage of their social evolution: hunting folk learn to fish and to make boats, cultivators learn to ditch and drain and irrigate, in early kingdoms men build canals and aqueducts and tunnels and wharves, and the same means for the same purposes seem to be found almost universally. But by the time peoples have reached the imperial stage, their whole civilization, normally, has become somewhat different from others. In law, religion, art, science, manners and customs, each step they have taken has been progressively influenced by the total milieu, so that the farther they have gone the more distinct has their total civilization become. Rivers, among other things, begin to have special significances for them.

In China, more than in most other countries, rivers and the uses made of them played a decisive role in men's struggle towards the community of a unified empire. At the time of Alexander's conquests in southwestern Asia, China as we think of it had never existed. Instead of being one culturally and politically homogeneous nation, it was a group of independent kingdoms which were in reality rival

187

economic areas. Each was based on some major river or the valley along part of its course, where rich grain land and ease of transport could make its people self-sufficient, and natural barriers could keep them isolated. Thus the valley of the Yangtze above the gorges was a separate entity from that in the plains below; it was possible for kingdoms to flourish in the Wei Valley and the middle reaches of the Yellow River without their people paying much attention to what went on in the huge flood plain of the river—actually a silt-built delta across which the Hwang Ho flowed to the sea, sometimes through one mouth and sometimes through another hundreds of miles away.

But in all these areas, as well as in the lowland between the two big rivers where the smaller Huai meandered, river control had long been a primary activity. It had begun, as in Mesopotamia, in the attempts of primitive farming folk to drain marshland, to irrigate the porous loess soil of the upper valleys during the many months of light rainfall, and to prevent devastating floods at the time of the heavy seasonal runoff. The typical engineering structure that had been evolved was the dike; it was born of necessity, from the fact that some sixty thousand square miles of flood plain around the lower Yellow River are below the level of the bed which the silt-laden river has built up for itself. Just as Mesopotamian legends told how the god Ninurta had "created the world" by building a dam to pen up the raging dragon of the floods, so ancient Chinese legends recounted how a culture-hero, "the great Yü," had brought order into human life by building the first dikes along the river's edge. The earliest historical record of such dikes is of those built under the direction of Duke Huan in the seventh century B.C., by means of which he united nine streams of the lower delta into one.

Five hundred years later, when the various warring

states of old China were first unified into an empire, water engineering had reached a very high development. As in the western empires, the engineer had come into his own; the names of master builders like Cheng Kuo and the father-and-son team of Li Ping and Li Erh-Lang are recorded by the annalists as carefully as those of their employers. Gigantic irrigation projects, such as the still-functioning system the Li family built around Chengtu, had been completed in many places in the upper valleys; the dikes had risen higher and higher across the flood plains; and the utility of canals, both for irrigation and for transport, was already a commonplace. It was a canal project, it seems, that actually started the wars which resulted in the unification.

When the kingdom of Ch'in in the Wei Valley, under a highly centralized and militaristic government, began to arouse the fears of its neighbors, two of them hit on the novel idea of using what amounted to a perversion of "technical aid" as a weapon of "cold war" in the hope of preventing a hot one. They secretly financed the hydraulic engineer, Cheng Kuo, with the understanding that he would go to Ch'in and persuade the king to build a great canal between the Ching and Lo rivers in order to increase the agricultural prosperity of his country. They were hoping, of course, that this kind of public works program would drain manpower away from his army and keep him too busy to think of conquest.

The trick worked, and the Cheng Kuo canal was actually built, but the diplomatic victory of the conspirators was short-lived. The newly irrigated land produced a great increase in grain reserves, and the new water-transport facilities proved to have strategic value for the army. Soon the ruler of Ch'in, more powerful and warlike than ever, conquered his rivals and brought the whole of northern and central China (the Yellow and Yangtze valleys) under his control. Then

> driven to find still further employment for the armies which he had formed, the first emperor pushed further to the south than any . . . Chinese . . . had done before, and in a campaign remarkable for its geographical extent, conquered the coastal province of Fukien . . . , the two Kuang provinces [Kuangsi and Kuangtung] and even Tongking in what is now Indo-China. This feat was made possible by the construction of a canal crossing the watershed between the Yangtze and the West River. (Joseph Needham: *Science and Civilisation in China,* vol. i, p. 101.)

Although the dynasty that achieved this first unification of China (222 B.C.) was soon overthrown, its work survived it, for under the succeeding Han dynasty (202 B.C.– A.D. 222) China remained a unified empire.

With the establishment of empire in China, there came a shift in emphasis in hydraulic works. It was not at all, however, the same kind of shift as occurred in the commercial empire of the Persians and was perpetuated in that of the Romans. The reason seems to be in the kind of tribute the emperors exacted from their subjects. The Persians, and later the Romans and the Byzantine emperors, collected gold; Chinese rulers, by contrast, have always demanded tribute in kind. With the peculiarly Chinese preoccupation with the real, the objective fact, they have in all periods required the peasants to send to their capitals the actual rice and millet they harvested, the pigs they bred, the vegetables and fruits they gathered from their market gardens. The bulk of the tribute was grain, and the movement of this grain to the capital became the fundamental concern of all the emperors. If the imperial clan, the numerous bureaucracy, and the army were to be fed, an elaborate transportation system for heavy shipment was a necessity.

The grain tribute is the fundamental cause of the development in China of the most elaborate system of waterways in the ancient world. The rivers themselves formed the skeleton of the system, but they were supplemented, and eventually connected one with another, by a maze of canals, built with great skill and maintained with vigilance. These canals were of course serviceable for irrigation as well as for transport, but whenever there was any conflict between the two the emperors ignored the needs of the peasants and concentrated their efforts on keeping the grain boats moving.

Floods of course endangered everybody, so that when the Yellow River dikes overflowed in 168 B.C. great levies of soldiers were detailed to help the farmers close the breaches. They may not have done their work very successfully, for again in 132 the river broke through to the south, pouring floods and vast quantities of silt down into the marshes around the Huai River. Apparently this time the damage was very slowly repaired, for some twenty years later the annalists describe how Wu Ti (the emperor who was in contact with Mithridates) made a tour of inspection and found the breach unclosed. Wu Ti did not depend on the soldiers alone; he dragooned thousands of local farmers, who had fought the river all their lives and presumably knew something about how to deal with it. To help them towards success, he sacrificed to the stream a white horse and a jade ring; then, to make assurance doubly sure, he ordered all the bureaucrats and court officials in his retinue to take off their silk robes and go to work, and stood by grimly overseeing as they struggled up the dike carrying bundles of faggots alongside the barefooted peasants. At length the breach was filled and the dikes made solid again, and Wu Ti erected a pavilion at the place to memorialize his triumph.

Despite such efforts, and despite considerable activity in making canals in the two principal valleys, the Han dynasty never built the one waterway that was essential if the empire was to remain united. This would be a canal stretching from the Yellow River in the north, across the plain of the Huai, and reaching the main stream of the Yangtze. It would be a genuine "lifeline of empire," because it would connect the self-sufficient economic areas. The Han seem to have been able to keep their urban population fed and their armies supplied with grain from the Yellow River Valley alone, and to have been content to hold the Yangtze Valley as a separate economic area merely by the force of their arms. Gradually, however, as the dynasty grew weak in the normal pattern of ruling houses, the Yangtze regions built up their economic strength to the point where they could revolt successfully. Around A.D. 222, the empire splintered into three kingdoms.

As soon as they were independent units, each of the three returned to the methods of Ch'in and began busily developing its waterways. Wei, the strongest of the three, built six major canals in those parts of the kingdom which lay in the Yellow River plains in northern China. Its kings, who also governed the Huai basin, realized the supreme importance of that region as a link with the south; there they dug two trunk canals, which were later on to be segments in the greatest of all Chinese achievements in hydraulic engineering: the crucial work that would connect the whole of the north with the rich Yangtze basin in the south by the longest artificial waterway men have ever built. Such a project could not be carried out when the country was divided. The three kingdoms exhausted themselves in fruitless attempts to reunify by force, but the result of their wars was only a worse fragmentation. There was no real unification again until the beginning of the seventh Christian century. When an "empire of all under heaven" was finally achieved again, the first effort of its rulers was to try to assure its permanence by beginning the Grand Canal.

In the year that the first Han was installed on the Throne of Heaven, Scipio Africanus, at the extreme western end of the civilized world, was ruthlessly plowing and sowing with salt the land on which, a few months earlier, had stood the Phoenician colony of Carthage. Carthage had to be destroyed utterly, as Cato had pointed out, because it challenged Rome's dearest ambition. When he made his speeches in the Senate, Cato had waved above his head, not a sword, but the branch of a fig tree, as the symbol of the insufferable offense of the city on the shore of North Africa. Carthage had managed to create in the deserts stretching back from her coastal site a flourishing agriculture, which was the foundation on which her maritime trading power rested. Rome was determined to exploit North Africa herself. In doing so, and in tackling generally the problems of water supply on which empire in the arid and semiarid lands around the Mediterranean depended, she was destined to build waterworks on a scale that would dwarf anything ever constructed before her time.

During their four or five hundred years of power, the Romans produced many brilliant engineers, and furnished them with unlimited numbers of slaves captured by the legions and sent in chains to the markets of the capital. Their huge constructions are still the most telling symbols of imperial greatness. When Shakespeare wanted to express the enormity of Mark Antony's rejection of Rome, he made the bemused general cry out: "Let Rome in Tiber melt, and the wide arch of the ranged empire fall." It is a superb phrase precisely because no other image could flash such a vivid impression of all the Roman empire means as that glimpse of a gigantic aqueduct striding on its ranged columns and wide rounded arches from end to end of the earth. Though we know now a great deal more than Shakespeare did of Roman law and religion and literature and private life, it is still the work of the engineers and slaves that gives us our clearest idea of what that relentless community achieved. (PLATE 11)

The reason we think of the aqueduct as a peculiarly Roman achievement is not that Romans invented it, but simply that they built so many and such large ones, and that their historians have talked so much about them. Sextus Julius Frontinus, who was appointed Water Commissioner of Rome under Nerva, and continued to serve under Trajan (i.e., from A.D. 97 to 104), wrote a whole book on the nine artificial watercourses which supplied the city in his day. The first had been built as early as 312 B.C., only a few years after the death of Alexander. At that time, Rome had been only a small city-state, whose inhabitants had for several centuries been able to take from the Tiber and a few springs all the water they needed. But from the beginning of their efforts in this direction, the Romans seem to have regarded an aqueduct as a singularly noble undertaking, and to have vied with each other for the honor of building one. Frontinus tells how the blind censor, Appius Claudius Caecus, schemed and connived to keep himself in office term after term, in order that he could give his name to both the Appian Way and the first of the huge waterworks that were to bring in distant springs for the refreshment of the city. Forty years later the Romans celebrated their victory over Pyrrhus by using the captured booty to build a second aqueduct.

194

As long as the citizens had any say in the affairs of the Republic, they continued to develop their water supplies, and many of the later emperors seem to have felt that an aqueduct anywhere in their dominions was a finer monument than a triumphal arch. Marcus Agrippa, the tireless builder of Augustus' reign, repaired the old aqueducts in the city and built several new ones; he was also responsible for the most famous of all such works, the channel that passes over the massive Pont du Gard to supply the city of Nîmes in France. At Lyons he got another aqueduct across a valley by building a siphon of rectangular stones cemented together. No fewer than thirty cities of Roman Gaul were supplied by aqueducts. Of the many in Spain, that built by Trajan at Segovia is perhaps the best known. Hadrian built them in Athens and in Istanbul, and he also constructed the splendid series of piers and arches which brought water from the spring of Zaghouan in North Africa down to the town that had grown up on the ruins of ancient Carthage, to be stored in renovated Phoenician cisterns.

> The Vandal invaders wrecked it, Byzantine engineers restored it, Spaniards demolished it, and finally the Bey, about the middle of the nineteenth century, brought it back into use, utilizing the old waterway where possible but adding modern construction and apparatus where necessary, to give present-day Tunis a perfectly safe water supply. (F. W. Robins: *The Story of Water Supply*, p. 67.)

Even the degenerate Caligula undertook to build two watercourses into the Imperial City, but Claudius finished them and pointedly omitted his predecessor's name on either, though he gave his own to one of them. By the third century A.D., Rome was drawing from fourteen aqueducts a daily total of some four hundred million gallons. The Romans in general, ever a practical people, seem to have shared something of Frontinus' own attitude towards these tunnels and elevated canals: "With such an array of indispensable structures carrying so many waters, compare, if you will, the idle Pyramids or the useless, though famous, works of the Greeks!"

As the aqueduct seems the very symbol of Roman practicality and the canal of Chinese worldly wisdom, so the cistern epitomizes more of Byzantium than merely its engineering. Again, the rulers of that eastern half of the former Roman empire were not served by inventors: cisterns had been built all over Palestine and Asia Minor as early as the rise of the first Phoenician trading ports, and even those remarkably inventive people were probably elaborating a method that had been in use long before them. Since they were skillful navigators and colonizers, however, they carried the science of cistern construction all over the Mediterranean world. In their principal colony, Carthage, many of the buildings of the city rested upon the roofs of large reservoirs quarried out of the underlying rock.

The tradition reached Byzantium, of course, through Roman models. Roman engineers, struggling to create in the deserts of North Africa a granary that could supply Italy, were quick to copy the Phoenician cisterns they found. What they built were, as I have written elsewhere,

> not mere storage tanks, such as we are accustomed to, but gigantic man-made caverns, hewn out of the rocky core of barren hills. Like the Carlsbad Caverns of New Mexico and other natural underground wonders, the Roman cisterns were composed of a series of huge chambers, sometimes as much as eighty feet from floor to

ceiling, connected by tunnels, galleries, and vaulted passageways. In their depths, water could be stored for years at a time, and taken out gradually as it was needed for irrigation.

To fill such enormous labyrinths it was necessary for the Roman engineers to devise means of catching every available drop of the scanty seasonal rainfall, and to do this they worked out an ingenious arrangement. They would first select some place where there was a natural cup in the hills . . . and erode the hilltops, flattening them out like roofs and throwing up earthworks around the sides, so that all the rain that fell could be channeled into gutters and then down through underground tunnels into the reservoirs below. By such methods they were able to take the water that fell on one acre in the hills and make it irrigate eight acres of productive land in the valley. (Brittain: *Let There Be Bread*, pp. 23–24.)

Such storage caves were built in many parts of the Byzantine empire. It was one of the few periods when towns have been able to exist in the desolate waste that is called the Wilderness of Zin by Biblical writers and is known today as the Negev, the driest part of southern Israel. From around 500 B.C. to about the time of Christ, the Nabataeans, an Arab people whose capital was the rock-hewn city of Petra, were able to grow olives and vines in that nearly rainless area by planting them in "dew mounds," an ingenious arrangement of piled-up flint pebbles which would condense the dew out of the cold night air and percolate it down to the roots of plants before it could evaporate. They also used small earthen dams to catch flash floods, and other devices. In Byzantine times, several cities flourishing in the Negev drew water from large underground cisterns.

It was in the city of Byzantium itself that the most splendid cisterns were built. There the plain, crudely hacked cavern became a piece of palatial underground architecture. The reservoir now known as Yerebatan Sarayi, built possibly by Constantine and restored by Justinian, is still not only a usable cistern but one of the showplaces of modern Istanbul. Three hundred and sixty-five marble columns, each over forty feet high and topped with an elaborately carved capital, support arches that carry the vaulted ceiling, creating when the water is low an effect like that of a vast drowned cathedral. This was only one of the numerous cisterns that assured the water supply of Byzantium, a series of structures that seem to symbolize the dank and murky splendor of that tortured civilization, hoarding up streams of enlightenment that had flowed down from the older empires, to grow stale in the darkness against the coming of the barbarians. (PLATE 12)

The variety and scale of hydraulic engineering projects in the ancient world indicate again that by the time of the emperors the significance of rivers themselves in human life had changed. Now that men were able to build so many kinds of waterworks, cities were not so dependent on the rivers for their water supply, nor were farmers for their irrigation. Just as, in transportation, the river had become now only a link in a system that included canals, lakes, oceans and land routes, so in the basic necessities the river was now supplemented by all sorts of manmade structures which could utilize rainfall, runoff, underground spring, and flash flood. In the older centers of agriculture, the river remained the primary source, but there the task of the emperors was simply to keep in repair the systems their predecessors had perfected.

The chief impression left by the waterworks of the imperial ages is one of sheer magnitude. Very little was invented. It is true that in making the great Chengtu irrigation system Chinese engineers devised movable dams and spillways in order to divert the Min River only at certain seasons. But what makes the whole project one of the wonders of engineering in the ancient world is the enormous cut that carries the river periodically through a mountain, and the 735 miles of artificial channels into which its waters are divided so that they may fertilize half a million acres of good land. In the early part of the Han period, if not before, adjustable sluice gates were introduced on Chinese canals, and these led to sequences of gates for the convenience of traffic, but there is no evidence that the pound lock, the really revolutionary invention, was evolved before A.D. 825. The imperial canal system impresses by its grandeur rather than by ingenious detail.

Finally, as we shall see, in the middle of the imperial age men of the Graeco-Roman civilization made perhaps the most important of all discoveries about rivers, but it was so completely revolutionary that the societies which brought it forth had to reject it lest it destroy them; it could not be brought under the shadow of the wide arch. On the whole, so far as water engineering was concerned, the empires did not encourage experiment; their achievement lay in developing earlier forms to staggering proportions. What their forefathers had done, men did again, but on a scale never dreamed before and unsurpassed later, until, in the most adventurous period the minds of men have known, the full resources of twentieth-century science could be brought to their service.

CHAPTER VIII

The Rivers Beyond

IN THE wide world of the deified emperors, the requirements of trade and the need of ordinary people for water were not the only factors that brought men into new relationships with their rivers. As they developed more ability to use it or to do without it, their attitudes towards the river changed also. A force that can be controlled or dispensed with does not command worship. With the increase of human mastery, the old river gods departed from their favorite haunts, leaving a gap in men's spiritual life that has never quite been closed. A science of medicine gradually displaced the water rituals and the healing streams, and even fortunetellers became less interested in the stain of sacrificial blood in a stream than in the fall of a tossed coin.

Since the nature of an empire is to expand as far as possible and then to hedge itself round with defensible borders, emperors are concerned to know what wide and deep natural moats their armies can reach and hold against attack, and where "the barbarians must be held back," as the Roman Hadrian put it, "not by rivers but by walls." The search for both trade routes and water boundaries brought many new streams into the consciousness of men, greatly enriching the general knowledge of the size and shape of the habitable world. With the sweep of armies and caravans out beyond the limits of earlier geography, men came to the banks of unknown rivers, and looked across them to nameless plains and mountains down the farther side of which must flow yet wilder streams—through what strange lands, and to what unimaginable seas? Confronted with such mysteries, men began to grow impatient with the myths that had pretended to explain the size and shape of the earth and the courses of its rivers. Out of that impatience came one of the major contributions of the imperial ages to human knowledge of rivers, that is, their effort to found a real science of geography.

The earliest attempt at a scientific description of the world, the geography attributed to Hecataeus of Miletus, was written just as the Persians were invading Greece, and it shows how little the Greeks knew before Asia was forcibly brought within their ken. Mesopotamia, Egypt, the Aegean area, and the sea lanes westward to Sicily and north into the Black Sea are fairly well described. But when the author gets across the Caspian Sea into Central Asia, his knowledge frays out, and though he has heard of the northwestern parts of India he does not know the Ganges. Until the Persians came, bringing gold that could travel anywhere, there was no pressing reason why he should.

As a result of the movement of men and ideas in the new order of things, within a century after this first geography was written Herodotus was able to weave into his great history an astonishing amount of geographical information. He knew the names and the general courses of hundreds of rivers, what kind of people lived along their banks and what were their customs, their traditions, and the products of their lands. He could describe for his readers the irrigation systems of Egypt and of Mesopotamia, could inform them that "the Indus is the only river other than the Nile where crocodiles are found" and that the curative properties of the Tearus are especially effective against scab, both of men and of horses. In an amazing geographical tour de force he could name all the rivers that flow into the Black Sea, from the Danube right round to

> . . . where Maeotis sleeps, and hardly flows
> The freezing Tanais through a waste of snows.
>
> (Pope)

He even knew, or thought he knew, the sources of all the rivers he mentions except the Borysthenes (the modern Dnieper) and the Nile, but comforted his ignorance of these two with the remark: "Nor, I think, does any Greek."

Admittedly some of Herodotus' "facts" have been corrected by later geographers; but the surprising thing about his book is not the occasional evidence of his generation's mistakes and misconceptions, but the extraordinary wealth of its information. Within fifty years, the importance of rivers in the new conceptions of the world was underlined by the appearance of a treatise entirely devoted to them. It was written by Ctesias, another Greek, who was court physician to Artaxerxes Mnemon. Although woefully inadequate by modern standards, it was sufficiently informative that it could still be used five hundred years later as a source book by the author of an essay on the subject.

From this time forward, knowledge of geography in general, and of rivers in particular, increased steadily. It was fed principally by traders' reports, as they struggled to extend their activities into new areas, and by the notes of men who began to go traveling for the sheer pleasure of discovery. Government officials like Megasthenes, or Patrocles who governed the Central Asian province for the Seleucids around 280 B.C., also sent back to the capitals a steady stream of reports from their distant outposts. Hanno the Carthaginian went out through the Gates of Hercules and some way down the coast of Africa; Pytheas of Marseilles explored the Atlantic coast of Europe, poking his prow into the mouths of rivers no civilized man had dreamed of, and sailing right round the British Isles. In other directions, men from the Mediterranean lands hunted part way down the east coast of Africa, crossed the Jaxartes in Central Asia, and began to use the rivers of India in their search for pepper and silk. And back along all these routes trickled the reports, sometimes factual, sometimes highly embroidered with sailors' yarns and fabulous tales, to be mulled over and sifted by stay-at-homes who were trying to construct out of them a rational geography.

One of the two best geographers of the classical period, Strabo, has carefully explained the importance of such reports. He himself was a great traveler—"I have traveled westward from Armenia as far as the regions of Tyrrhenia [Tuscany] opposite Sardinia, and southward from the Euxine Sea as far as the frontiers of Ethiopia"—and was rather smug about having actually seen more of the lands he described than most other writers.

However, the greater part of our material both they and I receive by hearsay and then form our own ideas of shape and size and also other characteristics, qualitative and quantitative, precisely as the mind forms its ideas

203

from sense impressions—for our senses report the shape, color, and size of an apple, and also its smell, feel, and flavor; and from all this the mind forms the concept of apple . . . And men who are eager to learn proceed in just this way: they trust *as organs of sense* those who have seen or wandered over any region, no matter what, some in this and some in that part of the earth, and they form in one diagram their mental image of the whole inhabited world. (*The Geography of Strabo*, Loeb Classical Library edition, vol. i, p. 453.)

As for the rivers he saw or heard of, they had become, to Strabo (c. 63 B.C.–A.D. 23), one of the two most essential features in any description of the earth; they and the mountain chains served, as he put it, to "geographize" a country. In describing them, he was scrupulously careful to distinguish fact from believable surmise, and both from pure fancy.

His successor, Claudius Ptolemy, who worked in Alexandria from A.D. 127 to around 140 or 150, has been called "so careless as to be worse than useless" on the subject of the rivers of the world. He is accused, for example, of neglecting all the major tributaries of the Rhine while mentioning a quite obscure one merely because it happened to be the boundary between two Roman provinces. But it may be observed that to the practical Romans for whom he wrote, that minor tributary was, after all, the important landmark they wished to know about; as for the streams we consider major, the chances are that neither Ptolemy, nor most people in his world, had ever heard of them. It is at least evidence of his concern with rivers that he is the first writer to observe the relationship between the Tanaïs (the modern Don) and the Volga, and to describe the latter correctly as flowing into the Caspian Sea. That people of the caliber of Strabo and Ptolemy should not have known many things that we know, or that Pliny's collection of admittedly tall tales should have outsold both of them, need not surprise us. What is really remarkable about the work of the classical geographers is the large amount of accurate and, to their contemporaries, valuable information they were able to assemble.

It would have been even more valuable if they had been able to exchange ideas with their colleagues in China. When the purpose of men is to found a new science, two civilizations are apt to be better than one; and the Chinese were making discoveries and perfecting tools that were unknown in the Mediterranean centers. About the time that Herodotus was writing, the rationalist Hsimen Pao was abolishing human sacrifice to rivers, and the shift away from superstition towards science was underlined by the scholars who were compiling the earliest surviving document on Chinese geography. "The Tribute of Yü" takes its name from a legendary hero, it is true, but there is nothing mythical about its attempt to describe nine provinces in terms of the kinds of soil found in them, their characteristic products, and the waterways running through them. It has been called, in fact, "a primitive economic geography." In the fifth century B.C., Chinese geographers knew very little about the whole country we call China, but they knew enough to begin with the simple practical facts about their various small kingdoms that were of value to farmers, soldiers, and government officials. After the first empire was established, they began writing official histories of each reign, and from around 20 B.C. each of these included a special chapter on the geography of the regions over which the emperor ruled. By that time, the first of the great series of Chinese books devoted to rivers was written (the "Waterways Classic"), in which 137 of the rivers of China are described. When this book was revised in the sixth century A.D., the knowledge of rivers had grown so much that it was enlarged to nearly forty times its original size. There is nothing in Mediterranean classical literature to compare with this encyclopedic work.

Another subject on which China could have taught the West much it did not know was the making of maps, for although cartography was apparently attempted in the Mediterranean world far earlier than in China it never developed to so high a degree of perfection. Curiously enough, the first mention of a map in Chinese records is in connection with the political skulduggery that went on just before the first empire was created. At about the time when two of the rival kingdoms were trying to divert the King of Ch'in from conquest by getting him to build the Cheng Kuo canal, another potential victim of his growing power tried the more direct method of assassination. On the pretext that the State of Yen proposed to make him a present of one of its provinces, an envoy arrived at his court bearing a silk map of the province in question rolled up in a bamboo case. At the climax of his presentation speech he unrolled the map and whipped out a dagger concealed in its folds. His trick failed, because the king's bodyguards reached him before he reached the king. And like the Cheng Kuo canal, the map only whetted the ruler's appetite for conquest, thus helping to bring about the first unification of China into one empire.

When he had made himself "emperor of all under heaven" a few years later, this Ch'in Shih Huang Ti ordered his officers to collect every map they could find in all his newly conquered realms. These maps were kept in secret archives while the scholars labored to perfect them. Huang Ti was apparently the first emperor in the world who had any visual record of the domains he ruled, and it is clear that he understood their value. His influence on map making continued after his death, for when his tomb was built in 210 B.C. its principal decorative feature was a magnificent map. "In the tomb-chamber the hundred water-courses, the Chiang [Yangtze] and the Ho [Yellow], together with the great sea, were all imitated by means of flowing mercury, and there were machines which made it flow and circulate. Above, the celestial bodies were represented; below, the geography of the earth." All this sounds as if Chinese technicians at this period had already produced a relief map, for the mercury must have flowed in channels and depressions. Relief maps were undoubtedly made later on, for there is a record of a general who, in A.D. 32, explained his strategy by means of a map in which valleys and mountains were indicated by relief modeling in rice. The rice-mound technique was widely used in succeeding centuries, and in the ninth an essay was written explaining how it should be done. One wonders if Huang Ti may have designed the map in his tomb himself, after the fashion of many Kings of Kings who planned their own mausoleums, to display what he felt was a major accomplishment of his reign. But whether he originated the art of relief mapping or not, he deserves to be remembered as one of the great patrons of the science of cartography.

The Han dynasty which succeeded his seized, along with the rest of his property, the secret archives in which Huang Ti had kept his collection of maps, and throughout the four hundred years of their rule it remained one of their jealously guarded treasures. When the redoubtable Wu Ti —he who had closed the breach in the Yellow River dikes and had sent his envoys and merchants clear to Parthia— invested three of his sons with the dignity of feudal princes, the most precious gift he bestowed on them was a series of maps of the whole empire which they would one day have to administer.

By the end of the Han period, map making in China had developed to the point where it could produce one of the world's great cartographers. None of the maps of Phei Hsiu (A.D. 224–271) has survived, but we have his own account of the work he did and the methods he used, and it reveals a knowledge and skill unmatched outside China for many centuries. He undertook to collect and revise all the earlier maps in the secret royal archives: "I have examined . . . the mountains and lakes, the courses of rivers, the plateaus and plains, the slopes and marshes, the limits of the nine ancient provinces and the sixteen modern ones, taking account of places where the ancient kingdoms concluded treaties or held meetings, and lastly inserting the roads, paths, and navigable waters." But in constructing a new map from these materials, Phei Hsiu worked out remarkably sound principles of map making: he used a scale, so that each inch on the map represented an exact distance on the ground; he used a rectangular grid, and the system of co-ordinates for locating places accurately; he took account of differences in elevation, and devised "means by which one reduces what are really plains and hills to distances on a plane surface," and ways of using geometric figures to get accurate measurements in rough country or over water where surveyors could not work. On the use of co-ordinates, incidentally, Needham remarks that "the very fact of drawing maps on silk would invite the suggestive idea that the position of a place could be fixed by following a warp and a weft thread to their meeting place." But however it happened, in Phei Hsiu's work mapping became an exact science, and the human mind made a long stride towards a rational comprehension of the world.

Virtually nothing of this splendid work, nor that of other

Chinese cartographers in the following centuries, ever reached the men in the Mediterranean area who could have used it to their great advantage. In the imperial ages there was not one civilization but several, self-sufficient and isolated, and they never achieved an international community in which the accomplishments of one could be known and usefully adapted in another. There were Chinese rivers, Indian rivers, and the rivers known to Romans, Persians, and Egyptians; but there was no science of rivers known to all.

In both Orient and Occident, many questions remained deeply mysterious. Although by this time the general shape of a river from its source to the sea had been deduced, and although a few had been explored throughout their courses, each new stream that was discovered immediately excited a host of questions. The most insistent was the query, "Where does it come from?" It is a strange preoccupation, perhaps, that urge to know where a river begins. Yet it seems to have haunted men at every stage of their discovery of the world, and to be especially strong at times of sudden expansion. The Romans never found the source of the Nile, though even Nero sent an expedition to look for it; that remained one of the most tantalizing mysteries in the ancient world, and indeed through all of human time almost to our own day.

Though the Chinese in their various imperial ages were also busy tracing their rivers, it was not until the seventeenth century that the great explorer Hsu Hsia-Kuo found the sources of the Yangtze and the West River, and discovered that Mekong and Salween are two separate streams. In the early empires, geographers were naturally more concerned with the Yellow River, since its upper valley gave access to the western areas where their traders and soldiers were extending their influence. For some reason, these early travelers assumed that a river in Sinkiang, the Khotan, must be the upper reaches of the Yellow; since they could trace no direct connection, they decided that it must flow underground through long stretches of its journey to the sea. This notion was generally accepted for some eight hundred years, until in A.D. 635 a general, leading his army up into Tibet to put down a rebellion, traced the river to a lake that is actually very near its source. Although Kublai Khan sent a scientific expedition to try to plot the whole course of the Yellow River more accurately, their ultimate goal, the exact spot of its origin, was never reached until Chinese scientists found it in 1952.

But as early as 852 B.C. had come the dramatic moment when Shalmaneser III of Assyria saw the source of the Tigris and knew that he had reached the fountainhead of his country's wealth and power. (PLATE 13)

> In the seventh year of my reign [he records] I marched against the cities of Khabini of Til-Abni. Til-Abni, his stronghold, together with the cities round about it, I captured. I marched to the source of the Tigris, the place where the water comes forth. I cleansed the weapon of Assur therein; I took victims for my gods; I held a joyous feast. A mighty image of my majesty I fashioned; the glory of Assur, my lord, my deeds of valor, all I had accomplished in the lands, I inscribed thereon and I set it up there. (Inscription on the Black Obelisk from Nimrud, quoted by Frankfort: *The Art and Architecture of the Ancient Orient,* p. 90.)

Shalmaneser was a warrior—like all the Assyrian rulers, a man who gloried in slaughter for its own sake. Yet Khabini and all his cities, which must have provided a hecatomb to the glory of Assyrian brawn, are passed over with a mere notation. What provoked joyous feasting, sacrifices, and mighty commemorative images was the discovery of the place where the water came forth. So fondly did the king remember this exploit that when he commissioned artists to engrave and emboss a representation of all his campaigns on the wide bronze hinges of his palace gates, only one incident is allowed to interrupt the monotonous chronicle of conquest. It is the scene of his great discovery, the one civilizing achievement of his life.

Despite such discoveries, and the evident satisfaction when they were made, the problem of the origin of rivers was not yet solved. For though one found the spot where the water gushed forth from the earth, there remained the question of how it got there. And men were equally puzzled to know where it finally went. How did it happen that although all the rivers run into the sea, the sea is not filled to overflowing? There were many curious explanations of these mysteries, but the most generally accepted was one that seemed to explain them both. It was that sea water finds its way back under the land through a vast network of cavities, tunnels, and fissures, whence it reissues in springs and river sources. In describing this supposed circulation of earth's waters, Seneca compares the passages to the veins, arteries, and canals of the human body.

Aristotle had pointed out that sea water evaporates, and the resulting rain clouds, along with the return of water through underground passages, apparently satisfied his question about the constant sea level. But it was another part of the problem that bothered him: he could not believe that rainfall plus subterranean circulation was sufficient to account for the enormous volume of water that pours daily down all the rivers of the world. So he decided that air also must penetrate into the earth through still other caverns, and the cold it encountered there must chill and liquefy it. Since most rivers, in his belief, rose in

211

mountainous country, mountains must be in reality honey-combed with ducts and siphons and condensation chambers. This reasoning produced a corollary: since most of the rivers he knew about were said to flow from the north, then the northern parts of the world must be high and mountainous.

This complicated theory was used later on in an attempt to unravel that other great mystery of antiquity, the source of the Nile. Vitruvius, the Roman architect and military engineer who wrote around 15 B.C., took the notions of Aristotle and combined them with a few hints from Strabo and with vague reports he had heard from heaven knows what source to produce one of the weirdest of all theories about the Nile. He was apparently so firmly convinced that all rivers must flow southward from sources in high mountains that he could not believe the Nile could actually flow, as it appeared to do, from a southerly source. So after naming all the other great rivers he has heard of, and pointing out that all of them rise "in the north," he ends his catalogue with a stream he calls the Dyris, which he says "comes from Mount Atlas" (that is, the Atlas range in North Africa).

> This river rises in the north [i.e., on the southern slope of the mountains], turns to the west to Lake Eptagonus and there changing its name is called Agger. Thence it flows from Lake Eptabolos under mountains of the desert through the south and flows into the Marsh so-called. It then winds round Meroe, which is the Southern Ethiopian kingdom, and turning from these marshes through the rivers Astansobas and Astoboas and many others, it arrives through the mountains at the Cataract. Thence rushing northwards it passes Egypt, between Elephantis and Syene and the Theban plain, and is there called the

Nile. (*Vitruvius on Architecture*, Loeb Classical Library edition, vol. ii, p. 149.)

Such were the speculations of well-informed laymen in the days when the science of geography was in its infancy, and naive as some of them were they served a purpose. Under the rule of the deified emperors, the world had grown incomparably larger; there were always new boundaries to be crossed, strange peoples to be dealt with, fresh markets to be opened, new routes to be discovered and made safe for traffic. There were eminently practical reasons why the geographers should be encouraged in their efforts to know and to map the coasts and the rivers and the passes through mountain ranges, and to deduce as well as they could the probable course of still unexplored roads and waterways that might lead to further expansion. The great fresco maps of the Roman empire that adorned some of the principal buildings in the capital may have been shockingly incorrect by modern standards, but they at least enabled men to think with a certain approach to realism.

In Hammurabi's world there had been one river, and the ancient Egyptians had had no word for people living outside their valley and delta except "nonhuman." Now there were hundreds of rivers, and they all flowed to the sea; there were hundreds of tribes and nations, and they were all human beings. If they could all be explored, all conquered, all brought under the shadow of the wide arch, perhaps a world of man might be created. Perhaps force and guile and emperor worship might turn the barbarians into customers and there could be peace.

That dream was never realized, of course; the empires did not create a community of interest that could be shared by mankind as a whole. But they did arouse in men the first glimmerings of a genuinely scientific curiosity about rivers. And such scientific inquiry as there was did produce certain bits of knowledge which men would eventually use to forge new relationships with the waters that flow over the earth. Exact knowledge of the source, the direction, and the mouth of a river is, of course, scientific knowledge, as are facts about its navigability, the roads through its valley, the towns along its banks, and the kind of people who use it. But the curiosity of men in the classical empires went beyond these rather obvious questions.

To take one simple example, the geographers of the period are not content to record simply that fish are taken from a given river. Strabo, like Herodotus before him, was particularly interested in the fact that different rivers contain different kinds of fish. "As for fish in the Nile," he records, "they are indeed many in number and different in kind, with a special indigenous character, but the best known are the oxyrhynchus, the lepidotas, latus, alabes, coracinnus, choerus, and phagrorius"—a list that may well have sounded as exotic to his contemporary readers as it does to us. The interesting thing for us is not the show of learning but the observation that Nile fish have "a special indigenous character." The point is made even clearer in his remarks on some information he picked up from one of his literary sources about salt-water fish that enter river mouths: "Aristobulos says that on account of the crocodiles no sea-fish swim up into the Nile except the thrissa, the cestreus, and the dolphin, but that there is a large number of different fish in the Indus." Herodotus had paired the Nile and the Indus as the only two rivers which had crocodiles, and it is clear that what aroused Strabo's interest is that rivers similar in one way should be so different in another. This kind of note taking is the beginning of science.

Ancient Indian literature shows a similar awakening of

interest in the fact that rivers are not all alike. Although river water generally is described as "transparent, light, stimulating, tasteful, appetizing, sweet, and lukewarm," Indian writers were at pains to point out that its properties vary according to the localities through which particular rivers flow. They observed that water flowing over rocky or sandy beds is more likely to be pure than that which flows over mud, and that the waters of sluggish rivers are heavy while those of rapid ones are light. This kind of thing may not represent a great contribution to science, and moderns may be inclined to dismiss it as scornfully as they reject the notions about one Indian river causing rheumatism and another curing it. But it is certainly nearer to science than the earlier Greek assumption that cows drinking from one river would produce black calves, while the waters of another stream would inevitably cause the calves to be red.

Of considerably more importance were a whole series of observations that scientists began to make about the work of rivers. There seems to have been little, if any, understanding in the Mediterranean areas of the way rivers erode the land. Working farmers may have understood it, for from very early times they were practicing terrace cultivation, which is a shrewd way of preventing one kind of erosion. The scientists, however, say little about it. The idea of a river cutting back at its head and carving out its own valley seems not to have occurred. But from at least the time of Herodotus, Greek observers were thoroughly aware of the way rivers bring down silt and pile it up at their mouths to form deltas. All the geographers mention this fact, and all were greatly impressed by it. Herodotus understood clearly that the Nile delta had been built entirely by the river itself, and the vast extent of its work filled him with awe; in order to communicate something of his feeling to his readers, he guessed rather wildly that if the Nile could be diverted into the Red Sea the silt would entirely fill it up in the space of some 20,000 years. Aristotle, a more cautious mind, was nevertheless disturbed by reports he had heard of how the Don was silting its mouth in the Sea of Azov, and predicted that in time this shallow "Lake Maeotis," as his generation called it, would disappear, leaving the Greek colonies at its head stranded far inland. In fact, most of the geographers seem to have been seriously worried about the possible calamitous effects of river silting; either that, or they took a special pleasure in frightening their readers with their predictions of deltas to come. At least they went out of their way to contemplate the enormous amounts of silt that were steadily pouring into the Black Sea from all its rivers, to announce that rivers pushing out from the Cilician coast would eventually build a land bridge clear to Cyprus, and to warn that the Achelous in Greece itself, which had already overtaken some nearby offshore islands, would eventually create an isthmus right across the Gulf of Corinth.

Apart from a fair amount of dredging of harbors and canals, it is not clear that these observations on the role of silt had very much practical result in the western countries. Egyptian and Mesopotamian farmers must have had some understanding of the nutritional value of silt, however, and it is certain that Chinese farmers did. Their knowledge of its fertilizing effect seems to go back to extremely early periods; in an ancient folk song they chanted:

Picks and shovels are as good as clouds,
And opening dykes is like bringing rain.
A *tan* [= 10 *tou* or bushels] has several *tou* of silt,
How it irrigates and fertilizes!

It makes our crops grow high
And feeds millions of mouths at the capital.

But as the centuries went on, farmers and scientists learned that silt, valuable as it may be, sometimes needs to be controlled. Across the thousand miles or so of its whole deltaic flood plain, the Yellow River, sluggish with its extreme burden of silt, slowly builds its bed higher and higher above the surrounding land. For centuries the Chinese had tried to keep control of the river by building their dikes higher each year, in a constant battle to counteract the effect of that steadily rising bed. But there was another school of thought among the hydraulic experts, men who began to teach that the thing could be better done by forcibly deepening the channel. These men argued, with Chang Jung (c. A.D. 20), that "the nature of water is to move downward; if it moves fast it will itself scour out its bed, and will scoop out great hollows and deep places." Fortunately, they did not all follow him to his bureaucratic conclusion that the way to solve the problem was to reduce irrigation and keep the waterways full for the transport of the grain tribute. Instead, they studied dredging, and for centuries Chinese river use was enriched by the results of fruitful argument between the partisans of high dikes and the partisans of deep channels. The over-all result was the amassing of a wealth of information in China about both the tearing-down and the building-up effects of river flow, much of it summed up finally in the epigram: "A good canal is scoured by its own water; a good embankment is consolidated by the sediment brought against it."

All these bits and pieces of knowledge about rivers and their ways had their effect, and undoubtedly increased the control men were able to exercise over their environment. Each had a certain value in itself, though its value in relation to other facts would not be fully realized until it could be fitted into the great synthesis of river knowledge which was achieved at the beginning of our twentieth century. Seen from our present point of view, some of the insights of the imperial ages appear startlingly modern. At certain points, men of the ancient world seem to have been almost on the verge of the great discoveries themselves. The control and use of silt, so much a concern of our modern whole-basin engineers, is a case in point. But a state of affairs in which the significance of all these various details could be perceived, and in which they could be related to one another in a productive framework of thought, would require many more centuries of patient work and a different organization of human society.

In the meantime, at the height of the imperial age, men made one more discovery, and it is in some ways the most important fact about rivers that has ever been found out. It was so revolutionary in its implications that its discoverers could not fit it into the pattern of relationships in which they lived; it would wait in the darkness for centuries before society was able to use it widely. But eventually it would provide the key to a world the empires never made.

CHAPTER IX

Rivers Enslaved

IF SPECULATION about the course of the Nile were all
Vitruvius had to tell us, he would be merely a curiosity.
But as a matter of fact, his book (its subject is really architecture) is one of the great landmarks in the history of
men's relations with the rivers of this planet. It gives us
the earliest scientific description we have of certain machines whose appearance is an event comparable with the
discovery of fishing or the art of drainage and irrigation.
For by his time, men had at last harnessed the power of
flowing water and made it perform work.

Vitruvius treats the momentous event quite casually, as
if a revolutionary increase in men's power over the environment were nothing remarkable. After he has finished
with all the important things an architect ought to know,
he finally writes what is virtually an appendix on various
machines that can be used for one purpose or another. In
the first chapter of his tenth book, he simply names a number of tools and machines which he says are well known,

and then, almost as an afterthought, decides to "explain, so that they may be known, machines which are *rarely employed*" (my italics). One of these machines is a water-lifting wheel which is turned by the force of the moving water itself, and one is a water-driven mill.

Ever since agriculture began, a very large part of the total work energy of the world had been spent in the performance of two onerous tasks, both absolutely essential for human survival. One was the necessity to lift a certain amount of water from rivers, wells, or cisterns, both for human and animal consumption and for irrigation; the other was the need to grind grain into a flour that could be used to make bread. The simplest way to do the latter is to spread out the grain on a flat rock and crush it by dropping another rock on top of it. The stone must be dropped again and again to make a handful of flour, and in the earliest days of breadmaking women spent an incredible proportion of their time down on their knees heaving up the heavy stone and letting it fall. Finally it occurred to somebody to lay the upper stone on the grain and shove it back and forth. This is still a hard and tiring job, but it is easier than lifting the stone repeatedly, and it produces a better flour. After long use, the lower stone develops a hollow in the middle, giving it a shape that has led archaeologists to call it a saddle quern.

While women were using these simple devices, men were working out ways of lifting water from rivers and irrigation ditches to pour over their fields. As we have seen, the machine they finally produced was the *shaduf*. Like the saddle quern, it required work motion in a straight line. Pushing and pulling, up and down or backward and forward, men and women used up an enormous amount of energy to obtain very small results, but the efficiency of their labor could not be increased until someone thought of applying rotary motion to the basic tasks.

Wheels had come into existence, as a matter of fact, some thousand years before *shadufs;* they were being used on vehicles in Sumeria around 3500 B.C., and very soon afterwards the potter's wheel was invented and universally adopted. Why it took so long for people to try using wheels of some kind in the tiring, everyday jobs is one of the mysteries. Possibly it was because rotary motion is unnatural for the human body. The limbs with which men work are composed of straight, hinged segments which move easily in straight lines; although the arm can revolve in the shoulder socket and the hand on the wrist, they have to be trained to do it and never do it very well. The few animals men have been able to harness are built very much the same way. Ancient men knew no way of producing work energy except by living muscles, and muscles can do nothing but contract and expand, moving bones up and down, backward and forward.

In any event, it was not until around 1500 B.C. that the irrigator got a machine which was easier to work than a *shaduf.* This was a simple pulley over which he could run his well rope. He still had to pull downward with a straight-line motion, but the rope ran smoothly over the wheel and a man could lift more water faster and with less effort. He could even tie the rope to an ox or a donkey and by driving it away from the well and back again could make it do the work for him. For the woman hunched over her saddle quern, however, there was no lightening of her drudgery for at least another thousand years. Heaving and sweating, the farmers and womenfolk hauled up the water and crushed the grain that nourished all the city-states and kingdoms and limited empires of antiquity.

It is surely one of the major ironies of history that the

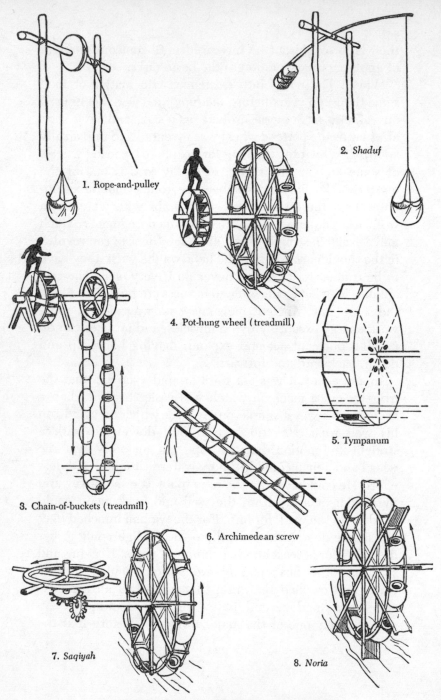

1. Rope-and-pulley

2. Shaduf

4. Pot-hung wheel (treadmill)

5. Tympanum

3. Chain-of-buckets (treadmill)

6. Archimedean screw

7. Saqiyah

8. Noria

EVOLUTION OF WATER-LIFTING MACHINERY

1. Saddle quern

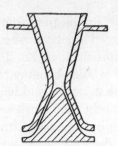

2. Rotary quern (Section)

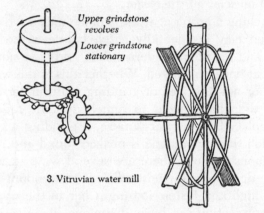

Upper grindstone revolves

Lower grindstone stationary

3. Vitruvian water mill

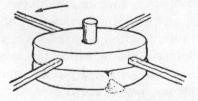

4. Rotary mill

EVOLUTION OF GRAIN-GRINDING MACHINERY

first significant laborsaving machinery should have appeared at a time when human labor was cheaper than ever before or since. Yet it was in the great slave empires, where the whole economy rested on labor enforced by the whip, that a rather sudden flurry of mechanical inventiveness brought such machines into existence. The process was begun by replacing straight-line motion with rotary motion. In the early machines this did not mean using any new source of power; it simply made the work of human and animal muscles a little easier.

Watching a potter at work, women may have seen a bit of dried clay accidentally catch between the revolving wheel and the board underneath it, and have noticed how it was at once pulverized. Whether this is the way it happened or not, the idea of grinding grain under a rotating wheel did finally occur to somebody. The saddle quern was replaced by a rotary quern, a grinding arrangement in which the upper stone is pushed round and round in a continuous motion. There are several ways in which this can be done, but the most efficient is to mount the quern breast-high and fasten a straight bar to the upper grindstone, projecting out beyond the rim like a ray. You can then walk round and round the machine, pushing against the bar, and grind your grain more easily. It would not take people long to discover that an animal can be hitched to the bar as well as a woman or a slave, and that its greater strength can turn a heavier grindstone and thus mill more grain. Rotary mills, in which the grindstones were equipped with several bars and pushed round by a group of slaves or donkeys, were in use in Rome around 200 B.C.

In the meantime, the simple rope-and-pulley evolved into a whole group of complicated machines for lifting water up from wells, ditches, and rivers. Here again the thing that lightened men's labor was a wheel that could be kept turning continuously by the power of the strong leg muscles. To invent such a wheel was a more difficult problem than the one solved by the rotary mill because in order to produce motion up and down the wheel had to be mounted vertically on a horizontal axle. It was solved by the treadmill, a wheel with a rim wide enough for a man or an animal to walk on. Mounted vertically, a treadmill can easily cause other wheels or pulleys to turn if they are hung on the same horizontal axle.

It may be that before treadmills were invented someone had already made a chain-of-buckets, an endless chain passing around two pulleys, one at the top of the well and one at the bottom in the water. Another form of the same thing is a single large wheel with buckets or cups fastened all along its rim (the "pot-hung wheel"). These two machines seem to be the first in which a vertically mounted wheel actually turned in water. Where they originated, and when, nobody knows as yet. It was once thought that the chain-of-buckets had been used to lift water for the Hanging Gardens of Babylon (c. 550 B.C.), but this now appears very doubtful. If such machines were in existence in the following century, it seems that an inquisitive traveler like Herodotus would have heard of and would surely have mentioned them. All we know for certain is that both the chain-of-buckets and the pot-hung wheel were in use in the third century B.C., and that both were then turned by treadmills. The chain-of-buckets was better for a deep well; the pot-hung wheel, for a pond or sluggish canal. Neither would be used in a swift-flowing stream.

In fact, that third century produced a whole collection of new water-lifting machines. Greek scientists, able to move freely about the world Alexander had left behind him, had opportunities of working in all sorts of unusual places and cultures, and of exchanging ideas with foreign colleagues. In the freer atmosphere, Hellenistic thinkers managed to break through the cobwebs of Athenian speculation and apply their minds to the solution of practical problems. Much of their activity centered in Alexandria, which was not only the greatest market place on the international trade routes, but was also the capital of the country that produced the largest grain harvest in the world by using a highly developed system of irrigation. In Egypt, water lifting and milling were of peculiar importance to the whole nation. For a man with a bent for mechanics, it naturally offered great opportunities.

To work well, a chain-of-buckets needs to run on pulleys that are fitted with cogs on their rims; the cogs catch in the open links of the chain and keep it from slipping back. The idea of putting cogs, or "teeth," on a wheel rim is said to have occurred first to Archimedes (c. 287–212 B.C.), perhaps the most brilliant of all the talented company who worked at one time or another at Alexandria. That he was interested in the problem of water lifting is shown by his invention of the Archimedean water screw. This machine is still used in Egypt, where the level of the canals is often only a few inches below that of the fields. Although it cannot raise water as high as the wheels, it draws a great amount in a short time. The only improvement it has ever needed is the modern crank to turn it, in place of the original treadmill.

Once they got interested in water lifting, the scientists kept hunting for better ways of doing it. In the century after Archimedes, Ctesibius of Alexandria found a remarkable one when he invented the force pump. This was a really great invention, but although Vitruvius included it in his list it seems to have been used hardly at all in the imperial age. It represented a reversion, after all, to the old principle of motion in a straight line. At the time, the whole direction of mechanical science was toward the perfection of machines that could use rotary motion efficiently.

Quite a number of these were tried at one time or another. One which greatly impressed Vitruvius was the *tympanum,* again a large wheel turning in water and driven by a treadmill. It was a big hollow drum with a very wide brim, divided inside into eight pie-shaped compartments; as it moved, the water was scooped up into each compartment in turn through a hole on the circumference, and discharged into a conduit through a smaller hole near the axle. Vitruvius remarks that although it does not raise water to as great a height as the pot-hung wheel, it does draw a large amount. We have no information about its origin, but it is clearly related to the screw.

Up to this point, the scientists were apparently encouraged in their tinkering and experimenting. Machines that depended for their motive power on treadmills or on walking in a circle could lighten drudgery, but they could not eliminate it. Rotary mills and pot-hung wheels and the ingenious water-lifting devices of the Alexandrians were all acceptable to the masters of a slave economy. They led, however, to something that was not acceptable: machines which were operated by a cheaper power source.

Here again, when we ask how and when and where men made the revolutionary discovery that rivers can do useful work, we come up against a mystery. Did some hard-working farmer place a pot-hung wheel in a swift-flowing stream instead of in the usual well or slow canal, and observe with some astonishment that it turned? And did he do it accidentally or deliberately, having a hunch that it would work? Or, on the other hand, was the first water-powered wheel the invention of a trained scientist? Naturally, the first mention of such a wheel occurs in a

227

book, and the book is supposed to have been written by a scientist named Philo of Byzantium, who lived at the same time as Archimedes. But there is some doubt whether Philo actually wrote the passage in question; it may have been inserted centuries later. Besides that, from the way the thing is put, there is no telling whether it records a new discovery or simply a use of something well known; in a long description of a very complicated chain-of-buckets, the author simply remarks that if conduits are made to debouch into "the cups of the hydraulic wheel," the whole apparatus can be made to turn. Certainly, if Philo did discover water power, he had not the faintest notion that it was a revolutionary event in the history of technology.

Similar uncertainties arise about various scattered remarks here and there in literature from the two centuries before Vitruvius. When the author of Ecclesiastes, for example, used "the wheel broken at the cistern" as a poetic image for death, he may have been recalling a treadmill-operated chain-of-buckets or pot-hung wheel he had seen; on the other hand, he may have been thinking of a simple pulley. The cistern could hardly have been equipped with a wheel turned by the force of a river.

The fact remains that Vitruvius around 15 B.C. gives the first clear description we have of machines that used any motive force except muscle power. Here is his account of the one that probably evolved first:

Wheels are used in rivers in the same way [as the pot-hung wheel]. Round the outside, paddles are fixed, and these, when they are acted upon by the current of the river, move on and cause the wheel to turn. In this fashion they draw up the water in buckets and carry it to the top without workmen to tread the wheel. Hence, being turned by the force of the river only, they supply what is required. (*Vitruvius on Architecture*, Loeb Classical Library edition, vol. ii, p. 305.)

This machine, which is nowadays called a *noria*, would seem on the face of it to represent men's first successful attempt to harness the power of moving water. It had apparently been in existence for some time before Vitruvius wrote; some scholars think it may have been first built in India, but all the evidence is extremely vague. The earliest representation of a *noria* that has been discovered is a second-century mosaic found at Apamea in Syria; only a few miles away up the Orontes River, at Hama, are the most famous existing examples, one of which is seventy feet in diameter. (PLATE 14)

In the *noria*, the stream could do man's work, and it was only a matter of time before a way was found to make it do woman's work as well. One very tricky problem had to be solved: before a wheel like this, mounted vertically in the water on a horizontal axle, could be made to turn a horizontal grindstone, it was necessary to have some means of changing the direction of the power that was generated. The cogged wheel of Archimedes offered the solution. Two cogged wheels mounted at right angles to each other form a gear, and a gear on the axle of a water-driven wheel produced the still more revolutionary machine which Vitruvius describes immediately after the *noria*:

Mill wheels are turned on the same principle, except that at one end of the axle a toothed drum is fixed. This is placed vertically on its edge and turns with the wheel. Adjoining this larger wheel there is a second toothed wheel placed horizontally by which it is gripped. Thus the teeth of the drum which is on the axle, by driving the teeth of the horizontal drum, cause the grindstone to revolve. In the machine a hopper is suspended and supplies the grain, and by the same revolution the flour is produced. (*Ibid.*, vol. ii, p. 307.)

The careful, if slightly awkward, effort to explain exactly how this contrivance is made and how it works may indicate that Vitruvius was describing a machine even more rarely used in his day than the others on his list.

The idea of gearing two wheels mounted at right angles to each other can also be applied to the problem of raising water, and sooner or later it was. If a vertical wheel turned by river flow can be made to rotate a horizontal grindstone, certainly the reverse action is possible. Men can be freed from the treadmill, and in their place an ox can plod round and round a horizontally mounted wheel to turn the familiar vertical pot-hung wheel in the water. The resulting machine is the *saqiyah,* which spread far and wide throughout the irrigating countries and is still in daily use. Vitruvius does not mention this machine, and the chances are it had not yet been perfected when he wrote. The earliest definite record of a *saqiyah* seems to be of one in Egypt in A.D. 114, some hundred and thirty years later. (PLATE 15)

The really revolutionary machines, however, were the water-driven, water-lifting wheel (the *noria*) and the water-driven mill. Except for the sail, they were the first machines that could do any of the work of the world by themselves, without requiring muscular exertion from man or beast. And the work they did was of the utmost importance, an absolute daily necessity in every household throughout the entire world. Water and bread must be had; for thousands of years, men and women had obtained them by the sweat of their brows and the ache of their tired muscles. Now, at last, rivers could take on the burden of supplying those daily needs, and men and women could be freed for the kind of creative work only human beings can do.

Yet Vitruvius says that the *noria* and the water mill were only rarely used on the eve of the Christian era, and the extreme scarcity of other references to them proves his statement. It was not because in Augustan Rome they were so newfangled: a Greek poet had described a water mill some seventy years earlier, and the *noria* is certainly older than that. Neither was it because they did the jobs any less effectively than older methods of "hand" work. On the contrary, the replacement of muscle power by water power meant a great increase in mechanical efficiency. The energy output of donkey or slave mills was not more than 0.5 horsepower; even in its most primitive form, the water mill Vitruvius described could produce 3 horsepower, and later forms were capable of yielding 40 or even 60 horsepower. Yet almost nobody used them, and they were seldom mentioned in polite society.

As usual, it was the poet who blabbed the secret discreetly kept by politicians, businessmen, and all others who had a stake in the prevailing economy. Antipater of Thessalonica, around 85 B.C., saw a water mill at work and realized the nature of the revolution it might produce. Being as "irresponsible" as poets usually are when they see a vision of the future, he promptly wrote an exultant poem:

> No longer lay your hand on the millstone,
> O ye women who turn the quern;
> Sleep long though the song of the cock
> announces the break of the morn.
> Ceres has commanded her water-nymphs to
> perform the work your arms did;
> They fling themselves upon the wheel and
> force round its axle-tree, which by

means of mobile rays rotates the mass
of four concave mills.

(*Anthologia Graecae,* IX, no. 418; Loeb Classical Library edition, vol. iii, p. 233.)

Water power, in other words, could free men and women from a great deal of drudgery, and that is precisely why the empires rejected it.

It is true that by A.D. 20 water power was used in China to run a mechanical contrivance for pumping bellows, and that this afterward was followed by water-driven trip hammers, which had a long and useful existence there. But throughout the first three hundred years of the Christian era, there were almost no efforts to use the new power source in the Romanized parts of the world. In the world the Romans had built there was no place for laborsaving devices or for the mass production they make possible. They had established slavery as the basis of the economy throughout their vast empire; their wealthy class had invested its money in land and slaves, and the slaves had so debased the value of labor that for the bulk of the free plebeians unemployment was a chronic state. Vespasian is said to have vetoed a proposal for building a water-driven hoist "lest the poor have no work," and many slaveowners vetoed water mills simply for fear their bond-women might grow fat and lazy. It was slavery, and the morbid fear of overproduction, that made the Romans delay for three or four hundred years the adoption of one of the greatest discoveries in the history of technology.

After the first Christian century Rome was on the defensive, and in the fourth century her affairs reached the stage of crisis. The empire was contracting before repeated inroads of barbarians; in A.D. 364 it finally broke in two. With a grossly inflated currency, the credit of the state disappeared, and the policy of free bread and circuses to keep the unemployed quiet could not be maintained. Worst of all, the retreating legions were taking fewer and fewer captives, so that the supply of slaves to the markets dwindled and finally ceased. The result was the first labor shortage the world had known for centuries. Free workers were at long last in demand, and they could ask for and get a wage. In order to depress that wage as much as possible by flooding the market, the Roman state finally, in 398, ordered a general freeing of the slaves. It had its temporary effect, but it was too late to save Rome from inevitable ruin.

In the meantime, a few employers had begun to solve the labor problem by using water power. There are not many instances, but we do hear of a large flour mill at Arles in the fourth century, a water mill for cutting and polishing marble in northern France in 379, and there is a tradition that water mills were introduced into India by Metrodorus, a Hellenized Persian, during the reign of Constantine the Great (324–337). Sometime later, Rome began to use water from her aqueducts to turn the old donkey and slave mills on the Janiculum. Athens in the fifth century had in the agora an overshot wheel, but although this type is more efficient than the conventional undershot wheel, it seems not to have been imitated. On the whole, this small flurry of attempts to use the power of flowing water meant little. The wide arch of empire was cracked beyond repair, and the greatest scientific discovery of the world it had shadowed could not save it.

It is never easy for people living in an economy that has produced a revolutionary advance in technology to make the changes in that economy which are necessary if the new invention is to be fully used. Rome's inability to make this adjustment was not exceptional. It was the

233

northern barbarians who, after centuries of struggle to become civilized, would finally make the river the prime mover of all industry. In the older centers, the wheel remained at the cistern, used almost exclusively as an aid in the ancient task of watering the dry fields. There, as the empires crumbled and fell, a certain continuity was maintained, but it was essentially a continuation of relationships that had been established before the empires had existed.

CHAPTER X

Wheels at the Cistern

THOUGH Egypt and Syria had early fallen under the Roman paw, the lands beyond the Euphrates were never consolidated into the western empire: Persia always managed to hold out and in intervals of peace carried on the great water-controlling techniques that had distinguished the earlier civilizations. When Shapur I fended off an attack from the Emperor Valerian in A.D. 260 by soundly defeating the Romans at the battle of Edessa, he carried off 70,000 legionnaires as prisoners. Arriving with this booty in Persia, he put them to work building what some have called one of the major engineering works of antiquity. It was a dam 1,710 feet long across the Karun River at Shushtar, built of granite and constructed in a way that twentieth-century engineers can still admire: the river first diverted around the dam site to give a dry bed for the foundations to be laid in, the river bed behind the dam paved with smooth stones, and finally great sluice gates installed to regulate the downward flow of the impounded water. (PLATE 16)

Shapur's most notable successor, Chosroes I (531–579) won a reputation with both Orientals and Europeans of his own time as a greater king than his contemporary Justinian. It rested partly, no doubt, on the fact that he held off the Byzantine emperors and for a brief time made Persia stronger militarily than it had been in the thousand years since Darius, but the more important reason for his fame was his work on domestic affairs. He seems to have had the energy of Sennacherib and the imaginativeness of Darius himself. He was constantly trying to improve the water supply of his cities and the irrigation of farm lands by repairing dams and canals and wells, and building new ones; roads were repaired and extended, with much attention to river crossings, bridges, and the linking of waterborne commerce with land traffic; and in his eagerness to get more land under cultivation he adopted what we might imagine is a modern practice of giving free cattle, seeds, and farm implements to anybody who would settle on wasteland and attempt to bring it into production. Chosroes (or Khosru as the scholars now call him) was definitely "good dynasty"; under his wise and careful administration, Persia enjoyed the last period of great prosperity it was ever to know as an independent country.

The pattern is always the same in the arid countries; when a period of peace is used as an opportunity for improving and extending the waterworks, when men turn back to the rivers, fostering and developing and intelligently controlling this richest of all their natural resources, then life surges up again out of the desert. These are the periods when trade and commerce flourish, when more and healthier people produce a fuller plenty, and when artists, scientists, poets, and philosophers adorn the time and assure its remembrance. On the other hand, whenever because of war or political corruption or general decadence the waterworks are neglected, then canals silt up, the fields shrink back before the encroaching desert, the rivers sweep down their valleys in devastating floods or ooze out through broken dikes to form malarial marshes, and the whole society of man flounders into a morass of poverty, ignorance, disease, and social stagnation.

The collapse of Rome and the weakness of Byzantium produced this kind of decline, in varying degrees, all over the Mediterranean world. Despite the efforts of Chosroes, Persia was too weary from long battling to make good her advantage. Though her ancient adversary was tottering, she could not muster strength to give the final blow that would make the Mediterranean once more an Oriental lake. Spain and North Africa were occupied by Goths and Vandals. Egypt, Arabia, and the Levantine coast were the lands where East and West had fought, ever since the death of Alexander, for control of the rich trade routes to India and China; by the time when Chosroes and Justinian were contesting, the inhabitants of most of them were exhausted. The old Nile-Red Sea canal had been allowed to silt up again; and when shortly before A.D. 570 the Marib dam in southern Arabia broke for the third or fourth time, the people who had repaired it frequently in the thousand years of its existence could not summon the energy to repair it again.

Throughout the world, the sixth century was a sad period. The great promise of international understanding and exchange that had flickered momentarily had for four hundred years been steadily fading. China, where the canals had never linked the Yangtze and Yellow River basins, seemed to be permanently divided into northern and southern kingdoms, each self-sufficient but engaged in constant warfare with each other. Absorbed in domestic affairs, the rulers no more sent their junks on voyages to the Euphrates, and they made fewer and feebler efforts to keep the Silk Roads open across Central Asia.

The Guptas in the same period lost their grip on India. The Girnar dam was repaired for the last time in 485 by a local governor serving under Skandagupta; the next time it broke there was no central authority to care and the local people let it fall into ruin. Even in the center of the empire, the later Guptas lost their control over the sluggish, silt-laden waters of the lower Ganges and the Brahmaputra. Their capital city, Pataliputra, built on low ground where four large tributaries join the Ganges, had been repeatedly flooded in the past, but after each visitation the silt had been cleaned out of the streets and its protective dikes had been heightened. Now the floods came and were not contested; water poured through the broken dikes and the city finally foundered under the weight of accumulated silt. Today it lies buried seventeen feet below the ground level of the present city of Patna.

In the west, as the epic struggle between Rome and Persia drew to a stalemate, the nations which had been pawns in the game all seemed to be going slowly downhill, waiting for some conquering migrants from the outer world of barbarism to come and revitalize them. No contemporary would have dreamed that recovery could come from within—that within a century one of those beaten nations would suddenly arise, seize an empire greater than either Persia or Rome had ever held, and quickly foster in it a civilization that could rival both.

Yet the Arab empire, and more particularly the Arab civilization, are not such surprising phenomena as they may at first appear. The initial conquest was made possible by the political vacuum. The civilization was essentially a revival of the indigenous culture; its builders were people who for two or three thousand years had been sharing in the river-controlling, water-using techniques that were the basis of all Middle Eastern civilizations.

Geographically, the Arabian peninsula is a wedge between Africa and Asia; from the earliest times its northern people had formed a natural link between Egypt and Mesopotamia. They had been gradually dispersing, so that by the time of the conquest there were large Arab communities all over Greater Syria and the Twin Rivers valley. Petra and Palmyra were both capitals of Arab kingdoms; large numbers of Arabs had lived for generations in Egypt; and Arab traders and colonists could be found from Asia Minor to Ethiopia. The inhabitants of the southern and southwestern coasts of Arabia were seafaring, trading people like their relatives, the Phoenicians. From very ancient times, they had controlled the sea routes to East Africa, forcing even the most powerful of the Pharaohs to buy frankincense from them, and later they had pioneered in the trade with India. Enriched by the daring of sailors and the skill of merchants, cities had risen in Southern Arabia and a high civilization had flourished. The Marib dam and the irrigation system it supplied were only the most famous of a myriad waterworks which provided amenities comparable with those in any other part of the Middle East. The world's first skyscrapers were built in Yemen and in the precipitous mountains of the Hadhramaut on the southern coast; to supply them with water, the scanty rainfall was conserved in huge bathtub-shaped reservoirs, made of so fine a concrete that it is still watertight, though the secret of its composition is lost.

At the time of the conquest, of course, both north and south were in the doldrums, like most of the surrounding countries. With their trade monopoly finally broken by the Romans, and their native paganism disrupted by the introduction of both Judaism and Christianity, the southern Arabians appealed to Chosroes to protect them against Ethiopian rivals, Byzantine overlords, and their native Jewish kings. Since the northern nomads were already paying tribute to Chosroes, the whole of the peninsula became a Persian satrapy.

When the small theocracy in northern Arabia, of which Mohammed had been commander and prophet, suddenly expanded within ten or twelve years of his death (A.D. 632) into a ruling caste acknowledged all the way from Carthage to the boundaries of India, they instantly set about repairing the damages that neglect of waterworks had brought upon nearly all their realm. That group of Arabs, the first Islamic conquerors, were indeed desert nomads, inured to sand and thirst, not skilled in the techniques of the riverine communities. But their banner was green, the vibrant green of the oasis that had always been the goal of their wanderings. "Do not the unbelievers know," the Koran pointedly inquired, "that from water was made every living thing?" Their passionate yearning for water prompted them to declare it the supreme gift of God, and to rule that the Right of Thirst conferred upon the humblest a divinely appointed access to the supply. For the good Moslem, as for the good Jew, the symbol of earthly reward for his righteousness was to be "like a tree planted by the river of water, which bringeth forth his fruit in his season." And the heaven to which he aspired in the afterlife was a land flowing not only with milk and honey but above all with life-giving water, where "the pious shall dwell among gardens and fountains . . . under an extended shade, near flowing streams." (Koran li and lvi.) It is small wonder that they should admire and try to extend what their predecessors had done with the rivers of the earth.

After the fall of Alexandria in 642, the first public act of Amr ibn-al-As, the conqueror of Egypt, was to clear Ptolemy's canal from the Nile to Suez, and send twenty ships down it loaded with Egyptian merchandise for the Arabian ports. Control of the Red Sea was quickly recaptured from Ethiopia and held by Arabs for over a thousand years, indeed until long after it had ceased to be the only sea route between Europe and eastern Asia.

When Khalid stood before Damascus a few years later, he promised the frightened citizens that if he entered their city "so long as they pay the poll tax, nothing but good shall befall them." From the point of view of people who for centuries had prospered or suffered according to the relationships their rulers had established with the waters of the earth, the promise was nobly kept. The Omayyad caliphs were no sooner established in Damascus than they set about improving the water system of that ancient and lovely city, doing the job so well that it still functions. The Yazid Canal (680–683) drew water from the Barada to create outside the city a lush oasis known as the Ghutah, a reclamation project so successful that it was celebrated as one of the four "earthly paradises" of the Moslem world. (PLATE 17)

In the valley of the Twin Rivers, immediately after the Omayyad viceroy had created the new province of Iraq, he began energetically on the same tasks as had occupied Sargon, Hammurabi, Sennacherib, and every other successful ruler the land had ever had; he renovated old canals and cut new ones, channeled the rivers and drained the marshes their vagaries had created, and began to irrigate vast areas of arid land on which impoverished native farmers could get a new start. At the same time, the Omayyad governor of Egypt was building a new Nilometer on an island near Cairo to replace the abandoned one at the site

241

of ancient Memphis. After the conquest of Persia, Shapur's barrage on the Karun was repaired and heightened, and made to serve a double purpose by having a roadway built on its top.

This kind of activity goes far to explain the immediate and lasting success of the Moslems. Although the two primary characteristics of later Islamic civilization are the use of the Arabic language and the practice of the Moslem religion, it was two or three centuries after the initial conquests before the bulk of the people in the conquered provinces accepted the religion, and probably equally long before they mastered the intricacies of Arabic and spoke it as their native tongue. But from the very beginning of their rule the Arabs spoke through their deeds a language universally understood, and practiced in their public works the behavior that had always been regarded in the lands they overran as the good life.

Through all the later ups and downs of Arab history, the swing of the pendulum is always indicated by the relative attention paid to river control and water conservancy. When a revolt is successful and results in a new dynasty or caliphate, it is inevitably signalized by great activity centering round waterworks; there is then a "golden age" in which the people enjoy a prosperity based on rich agriculture and trade; then the energy slackens, building and harbor construction cease, and depression follows depression until the decadent government is replaced by one which consolidates its power through renewing the ancient activities.

When the Abbasid caliphs seized control of affairs, one of the few surviving Omayyads fled to Spain (A.D. 756), quickly conquered most of it, and immediately began to beautify his capital of Cordova, bringing it fresh water through a great aqueduct from the mountains, enlarging the old Roman bridge over the Guadalquivir to the full glory of its seventeen arches, and laying out gardens along the river bank where fountains tinkled and artificial lakes reflected the walls and towers of his palace. Under his namesake and successor, Abd al-Rahman III (912–961), his dynasty reached its height, and the splendor of Cordova and its great river port of Seville were the admiration of the world. Queen of Europe in the tenth century, Cordova was an unrivaled center of learning and culture; in medicine, philosophy, literature, music, and many sciences it created much and transmitted more. But perhaps the most permanent contribution of Moslem Spain to world civilization was its agriculture. On the hot, dry slopes of the peninsula, Middle Eastern methods of irrigation made possible the growing of Middle Eastern plants: rice, apricots, peaches, pomegranates, oranges, sugar cane, cotton, and saffron were all introduced into Europe through the gardens Abd al-Rahman and his successors planted.

The greatest center of Moslem power through many centuries was of course Baghdad, the city Mansur founded in 762 in that same valley of the Twin Rivers which had seen Ur and Akkad, Babylon and Nineveh, Seleucia and Ctesiphon. It lay beside the turgid, yellow waters of the Tigris, where that river approaches within thirty-five miles of the Euphrates, with which it was connected by a network of canals. Strategically placed, like all the ancient Mesopotamian cities, to dominate profitable trade routes, Baghdad under the Abbasid caliphs became the most important city in the world. In the person of Harun al-Rashid (786–809) was concentrated more power than in any other contemporary.

And like all its forerunners, its greatness and indeed its very existence depended on the rivers. We remember Baghdad in its glory for its literature, its wealth, its scientists and philosophers, the blackness of its intrigues and the gorgeous color of its mosques and bazaars and harems —for Ali Baba and Sindbad and Aladdin, and the tales of Harun wandering disguised at night through the streets, listening to his people's opinions. But all these were results of Baghdad's greatness, not causes. The basis of all that splendor and squalor was the muddy river, with the round black coracles Herodotus had observed at Babylon still bounding and whirling on its surface, the lumbering inflated-skin rafts floating down from Mosul, the ferry-boats plying from shore to shore, and Arab dhows, Indian craft, and Chinese junks laboring up from the Persian Gulf against the swift current to unload their wares on the docks.

The primary food of Baghdad was a fresh-water fish, just as it had been in all the ancient capitals; in this instance, a sort of tunny called *biz* which was taken in huge nets from the Diyala River. Harun returning from his nightly rounds would doubtless see in the early dawn shipments of these enormous fish being unloaded at the wharves, each fish so large that it required a mule to carry it. And as the morning came on, the streets of Baghdad would begin to ring with the cries of the mule drivers guiding their long lines of animals to the fish market. Those mule trains were the lords of the way, for whom all stood aside. All the traffic in Baghdad's streets was important to the city: the donkeys with their tinkling bells and their glistening black water-skins, the camels coming from the desert caravan routes, the crowds jostling each other in the bazaars, the merchants haggling over spices and silks. But all gave way before the mule trains that carried the city's basic food. (PLATE 18)

Arab civilization, like all the Middle Eastern cultures that it welded into a new synthesis, was essentially riverine. It was never centered for long on a single river-based city, but each of its many capitals owed its life and its power to the relationships men had established with some river, large or small, from Bokhara and Samarkand on the trade route between Oxus and Jaxartes, to Cordova on the Guadalquivir, or Cairo on the Nile. Along these rivers, the caliphs and sultans and ruling dynasts worked by fits and starts at the tasks of river control and river use that had determined the rise and fall of all their predecessors.

For all the achievements of the common Islamic civilization in other directions, little if any advance was made in the techniques of this basic preoccupation. The Arabs did all the things Sennacherib had done, and as far as water supply and irrigation were concerned they did them in much the same ways. Dams, aqueducts, canals, cisterns they built industriously, but there is no evidence that their engineers developed any new principles of construction or found out anything about their craft which had not been common knowledge for generations. When in some part of their enormous empire they found some useful local technique, they adopted it and tried it out in far distant lands; an example is their diffusion of the Persian *qanat* throughout North Africa. But as in other departments of human activity, the historic role of Arab civilization was not to push river technology forward into a phase that would remake human life, but to preserve the achievements of the past and hand them on to the future.

Nevertheless, in determining the role of rivers in the human adventure and in preparing for the enormously fruitful relationships men would eventually establish with flowing streams, the Arabs did suggest some important ideas. For example, the system of water laws that grew up from principles laid down in the Koran and the Traditions remains one of the world's great formulations of legal thought. It took deep hold upon the minds of men throughout the whole area over which Islam spread its green banner, and the reason is not far to seek. Although more elaborate than any that had preceded it and representing at certain points higher ethical concepts than most of them, its roots reached back to Hammurabi's Code and its highest branches did not overtop the precepts of Solomon. For our own day, its significance goes beyond the fact that it is still accepted unquestioningly by millions of people: more important is its basic principle that water, being the gift of God, may not be sold. Though all who have need of a river may use it, no one may own it, and none may make a profit by selling its waters.

This principle undoubtedly stood in the way of certain kinds of technological development; with many other factors that prevented the profit motive from operating, it served to discourage industrialism, to keep Islamic society "ancient," more closely akin to the civilizations of antiquity than to the machine civilization of the modern world. On the other hand, it is clearly in harmony with much of our best contemporary thinking about river control and valley development. Underlying modern theories of conservation, and giving moral sanction to the most advanced schemes of co-operative endeavor, are ethical principles no different, in essence, from the Moslem doctrine. After more than a thousand years, it was fitted into the twentieth-century synthesis when Theodore Roosevelt proclaimed that all the potential value in any river belongs of right to the whole people.

Another insight that seems peculiarly appropriate to our modern notions has to do with measures for insuring public health. The Moslems did much in this direction, building the first public hospitals, the first schools of pharmacy, and the first traveling clinics, and pioneering in measures for

246

insuring public hygiene. In the tenth century, physicians in Baghdad had to undergo examinations and secure a license to practice, and some of them were required to make daily visits to patients in the city's jails. It need come as no surprise, therefore, that their illustrious philosopher-poet-scientist, Avicenna, made one observation of fundamental importance to river-using communities when he noted the role of flowing water as a spreader of contagion. A few years later, in 1073, Baghdad was devastated by one of the worst floods it ever suffered, and in cleaning up the city the Seljuk sultan, Malikshāh, put into practice Avicenna's ideas. He ordered that the dirty water from the public baths was no longer to be dumped into the Tigris, but diverted into cesspools; and he set aside special places, well back from the river, for the cleaning and curing of fish. Avicenna's precept is of course fundamental to modern public sanitation and is taken account of in all well-planned river projects at the present time.

Apart from such innovations, the role of rivers remained very much the same under the Arabs as it had been in the earlier empires. Like them, the Arab world was a richly cosmopolitan one, in which a remarkable variety of peoples were able to live, to travel, and to trade with considerable freedom. Arabic as the official language served the same unifying purpose as Aramaic in the empire of Darius, Greek in the Hellenistic period, and Latin under the Romans. Trade flourished, and was assisted by the more energetic rulers with public work on roads, bridges, and waterways. With an eye on the strategic position of Egypt astride one of the great maritime routes, Harun al-Rashid talked seriously of cutting a Suez canal straight through the Isthmus, anticipating the work of de Lesseps by a thousand years. Although he was finally dissuaded by his prudent treasurer on the ground that such a waterway could never repay its cost, the idea remained in the world's mind.

Piety, rather than commerce, was the motive that prompted Harun's wife, the famous Queen Zubaida, to undertake the project that is her most lasting monument. Along the whole extent of the pilgrim road from Baghdad to Mecca, she ordered the construction of a series of wells at convenient intervals, so that the faithful might come at each night of their pilgrimage to a pleasant oasis where they might refresh themselves for the next day's journey. As a result, her praises were sung by travelers for centuries.

There was far more traveling in Islam than there had been in earlier dispensations. The obligatory pilgrimage to the Holy City, the traditional "journey in search of learning" which every serious scholar aspired to make, the deep-rooted Arab love of the sea and skill in navigation, and the instinct for trade all encouraged it, and the devotion to books and talk brought a wide diffusion of knowledge picked up on the way. "Describe for me the lands of the earth," the Caliph Omar had instructed the scholar, "their climates and positions, and the influences which ground and climate exert upon their inhabitants." The injunction seems to have been taken to heart by all the host of travelers and geographers who in the succeeding centuries built up a more complete knowledge of lands and peoples than men before them had possessed. Descriptive geographies, encyclopedias, travel tales, road maps and charts poured forth in a flood. The Arabs went everywhere, and when they could not go in person, like the Sicilian geographer Idrisi they sent trained observers to bring back accurate firsthand reports from every land they could reach. The Volga became as well known to readers in Iraq and Spain as the Ganges and Danube, and the east coast of Africa was more familiar than the western coast of Europe.

Most important of all, the Arabs from the beginning of their dominance established contact with China, and through many centuries were able to keep up trade and intercourse among the great centers of ancient civilization: China, India, and the regions we call the Middle East. Sweeping up through Persia and consolidating their rule over Central Asia to points far east of the Jaxartes River, they were able to give safe conduct once again to caravans coming westward from the centers of Chinese culture. At the same time, being even more daring navigators than the Greeks whom the Romans had employed, they undertook ocean voyages all the way around India and Southeast Asia to Canton. The first Arab embassy arrived in China, by sea, in A.D. 651, only nineteen years after the death of Mohammed.

China at the time was entering her golden age. At the beginning of the century the rulers who constituted the short-lived Sui dynasty had created a unified empire once again and had consolidated it. The first of these, the conqueror Yang Chien, had brought under his rule the whole area from Annam northward to the Great Wall, and from Tashkent in Central Asia to the island of Formosa in the Pacific Ocean. His military exploits created the semblance of unity; the water-control works of his successors, Wen Ti and Yang Ti, made it a reality.

These rulers were northerners, with their political capitals at Loyang on the Yellow River and Chang-an (Sian) on one of its major tributaries. But the strongest economic area was south of there, in the valley of the Yangtze below the gorges. To keep the country unified, and to bring the all-important grain tribute to the court and the bureaucracy, the first political necessity was to build a transport system that could link the center of production with the center of power. This is exactly what the Sui emperors accomplished: at an appalling cost in human labor and life, Wen Ti built a great canal northward from the Yangtze to the Huai River that drains the wide plain lying between the two major valleys; Yang Ti extended it on to the Yellow River in the north, improved it all along its course, and south of the Yangtze made connections with rivers in the southerly plains. The resulting inland waterway, with its roads on both banks, its shadowing elms and willows all along the route, and its imperial rest houses between every two post stations, formed the backbone and major portion of what came to be called the Grand Canal.

Many tales are told of the ruthlessness with which the Sui emperors pursued their goal: five and a half million workers are said to have been commandeered for the job, and every fifth family in the whole of the empire required to contribute one person to help supply and prepare the food such a company required. As one Chinese historian sagely remarked, the public works of Yang Ti "shortened the life of his dynasty by a number of years but benefited posterity to ten thousand generations. He ruled without benevolence, but his rule is to be credited with enduring accomplishments." He was quickly displaced by the T'ang rulers, who during the three centuries of their reign wisely kept up the canals he had built.

For a thousand years succeeding dynasties continued to work on that longest of man-made waterways, flourishing when they kept it navigable and declining when they neglected it and the other water-control measures that made China's plains productive. When Europeans eventually "discovered" China, the most remarkable of all the wonders reported by such travelers as Marco Polo was that incredibly long canal that had been dug by human hands. The Grand Canal reached its greatest development around the seventeenth century, under the later Mongols. Today its restoration figures largely in the plans of the Chinese People's Republic.

The T'ang emperors seem to have welcomed the Arabs and for several centuries there was much fruitful intercourse between east and west. It was one of the periods, according to Needham, when the Chinese have been most interested in other lands, and most receptive to foreign influence.

Chang-an, no less than Baghdad, became a meeting-place of international fame. Arabs, Syrians, and Persians came there from the west to meet Koreans, Japanese, Tibetans, and Tonkinese, and to discuss religion and literature with Chinese scholars in the elegant pavilions of the great city in the Wei Valley. It became a commonplace for wealthy Chinese to employ Central Asians as grooms and camel-drivers, Indians as jugglers, Bactrians and Syrians as singers and actors. (Needham: *Science and Civilisation in China,* vol. i, p. 125.)

All this contact brought about a certain amount of exchange in science and mechanics, as well as a rich trade. Certain results of the Arab-Chinese intercourse were of lasting benefit to world civilization generally. For example, the Chinese art of papermaking was introduced into the Arab lands around the middle of the eighth century. The Moslems then proceeded to improve on the invention by perfecting a way of making paper from rags, and this made possible its later spread into lands where neither silk nor papyrus could be produced. By the early tenth century, papyrus went out of use in the Mediterranean area; when parchment was later abandoned in Europe, it was rag paper, introduced by the Arabs, that took its place.

In the rich period of the T'ang and the Abbasids, however, there is one very surprising lack: neither of these ingenious, inventive peoples seems to have developed the use of water power very far. The Graeco-Roman discovery was certainly known to the Arabs, for at a fairly early period the works of Philo, Vitruvius, and other writers on mechanics were translated into Arabic, usually by Syrian Christians and Jews, so that the information necessary for wide use of mills was available. Many scientists in the Arab world were fascinated by various amusing toys in which water power caused wooden birds to squeak or a hydraulic organ to play a tune. In places the Arabs did build a few *norias* to supply baths, fountains, and irrigation canals, and by the tenth century a fair number of water mills were in existence. These mills, however, never meant in Islamic civilization anything like what they were to mean in European. Even in the tenth century, water-powered corn mills were far more numerous in backward Europe. Furthermore, and this was the crucial point for the future, the Arabs never applied the inexhaustible power of the river to other tasks. They were willing to use it for lifting water, though even there the *saqiyah* was the standard machine; and they built a number of floating mills, particularly on the Tigris, to grind grain. But it never seems to have occurred to them that running water could become the prime mover of an industrialized society.

There are many reasons for this seeming neglect. Slavery still existed on an enormous scale, and doubtless played its part in discouraging laborsaving inventions. More importantly, perhaps, the Arab genius is not particularly suited to mass production and the values it inculcates. The typical product of Arab craftsmanship is the *objet d'art*, hand-wrought with fine skill and loving attention, just as the typical product of the civilization as a whole is the poem. "Wisdom has alighted on three things: the brain of the Frank, the hand of the Chinese, and the tongue of the

Arab." The lands in which Arab civilization flourished are another factor that discouraged water-powered industrialization: most of the rivers are either wide streams meandering slowly across a desert plain, or occasional and uncertain torrents that rush down normally dry wadis. For example, from the sea right up to the first cataract of the Nile, six hundred miles above Cairo, there is no good power site. Windmills, which the Arabs found in use in Persia, are more appropriate sources of energy in those countries than water mills; they were fairly widely adopted, and seem to have supplied all the mechanical energy the society required. The structure of that society and the Islamic laws under which it lived prevented the rise of a manufacturing class which could make personal profit from exploiting water power. And finally, there was the deep-seated prejudice against enslaving so pure a gift of God: "How could we," asked the pious citizens of Ijli in Morocco, "compel the sweet water to turn a mill?"

With the Chinese, matters stand somewhat differently. Realistic, practical, with highly inquisitive minds and clever hands, the Chinese would seem to be, of all the anciently civilized peoples, the ones most likely to have made a swift and easy transition into the modern world. Considering the course their civilization had taken up to its golden flowering under the T'ang, one might have predicted that they would speedily transform their community into an industrialized society, with water power as its prime mover.

Their failure to do so was not owing to ignorance of the basic principle: within fifty years of Vitruvius' work, the annals record that "Tu Shih . . . invented a water-power blowing engine for the casting of metal agricultural implements." This sounds as if the discovery of water power in China may have been made completely independently of

253

any developments in the West. In any event, it was not forgotten, for two hundred years later "Han Chi adapted the furnace bellows to the use of ever-flowing water, and an efficiency three times greater than ever before was reached." This is surprising enough in itself, for a contrivance that can use water power to pump bellows sounds, at first notice, like an extremely complicated machine, the sort of thing one would expect to result after a long evolution of mechanical forms. But at the same time, the Chinese were applying water power to other uses, some of which were unknown in Europe for over a thousand years. Water-driven trip hammers, for example, are first mentioned in China around A.D. 20 and are referred to frequently in the following centuries.

In China, in other words, water power seems to have originated, not in connection with the old tasks of water lifting and milling, but in the hard work of metallurgy. Before the Han period, Chinese farmers apparently lifted water by hand; then, after brief experiments with the rope-and-pulley and the *shaduf*, they perfected their own characteristic machine, the square-paddle chain pump. This is a sloping trough up which the water is pushed by a succession of paddles fitted on to an endless chain. It was turned originally by a man, either stepping on the paddles themselves or walking in a treadmill attached to the axle of the upper wheel. Fairly late in history, animals were used—the first illustration is from the twelfth century—and still later the machine was occasionally adapted to water power. As for water-driven grain mills, the evidence is very hazy; there were certainly a good many in use by the time the Arabs reached China, but they probably originated later than the bellows and trip hammers and, as we shall see, may have had no connection with them.

All this is very puzzling, for the development of water

power in China does not seem to follow the patterns noted anywhere else in the world: the original discovery of a self-moving water-lifting wheel, then the adaptation to grain milling, and finally the extension of the principle to a multitude of uses in industrial processes. Industrialization, which came in Europe as a result of applying water power to a myriad tasks, did not occur in China until the twentieth century, by which time other sources of energy were available. A few industrial processes, and those in the vitally important metal trades, were powered by water for a long time, apparently, before the river was used in the essential food-producing jobs. Yet the machines were never generalized, the power source never applied to a wide diversity of processes.

Part of the explanation may lie in the kind of machines the Chinese used. Pumping bellows or causing trip hammers to strike requires straight-line motion. The best explanation of Tu Shih's invention is that it was a lever working on the same principle as a *shaduf*: when one end was forced down, the other was pushed upwards against the bellows. In order to make water force one end down, Tu Shih apparently fitted it with a scoop. Water pouring down into this scoop would make it descend, and when it reached the bottom and poured out the water it would rise again. The water would obviously have to be controlled so that it flowed into the scoop intermittently. If this is the way it worked, then Han Chi's adaptation, which obtained its greater efficiency by using "ever-flowing water," would have consisted in building a kind of rimless wheel, in which each spoke ended in a scoop. The resulting wheel would be very similar to the vertical wheel of the Mediterranean world, and since it would be placed in a waterfall to use the water's weight as well as its flow, it would constitute a primitive form of the "breast wheel" developed so many centuries later in Europe. It could have been easily adapted to furnish power for any kind of machine in which another wheel was mounted vertically on the same axle, such as a sawmill; with gearing, of course, it could produce rotary motion in the horizontal, as for turning grindstones. In either use, it would furnish a fair amount of power efficiently.

Yet this development did not follow, and the reason may be that the Chinese had a different conception of what constituted a water mill. All the scholars seem to agree that the characteristic Chinese form for a water-powered grain mill was entirely distinct from the Vitruvian mill of the West. Instead of the vertical wheel mounted on a horizontal axle, which is very easy for a river to turn, they think that the Chinese, at some early period and quite independently, invented for the purpose of grinding grain a horizontal wheel, not lying in the river but forced round by a jet of water striking against blades or into scoops along its rim. Such a wheel has one great advantage: it does not require any gears, since a grindstone naturally lies in the horizontal and can be mounted on the same axle. But its limitations are so serious that it cannot be adapted to industrial purposes. Most of the power in the moving water is lost; the inefficient wheel turns very slowly, grinding in a whole day only enough flour for one family, and it is incapable of being made more powerful. Such wheels were later used in Europe, but only by individual peasants for home consumption. They cannot provide the impetus for industrial development because it is virtually impossible to do any work with them except grind a handful of grain. It is true that the horizontal water wheel eventually gave the first clue for our highly efficient modern turbine, but only after many centuries of scientific development showed men the possibility of using an entirely different principle. In itself, the horizontal water wheel is a dead end so far as the evolution of mechanics is concerned.

Apart from these mechanical difficulties, there was much in Chinese society itself to hinder industrialization on a large scale. The bureaucratic structure of the government, the emphasis on the use of waterways for moving the grain tribute, and the absence of the profit motive all militated against it. Irrigation, flood control, and transport were more important activities in Chinese society than manu facturing, and when the needs of water-powered industry conflicted with these it was the mill that had to give way. In A.D. 764 the government ordered seventy mills completely destroyed, and fourteen years later did away with eighty more. After a further two centuries, all milling was brought under the control of bureaucratic commissions in order that it might be kept subservient to the general water-conservancy programs.

On the whole, the Chinese were content to establish with the great rivers of their land very much the same relationships as those which had characterized the Indian and the older Mediterranean cultures. The rivers served the same purposes of water supply, fisheries, irrigation, sewage disposal, and above all as means of transport, and because of their obstreperous nature they called forth even more strenuous efforts at flood control.

As to mental attitudes, the Yangtze and Yellow and Huai were never approached with the same awe or mystic adoration as rivers like the Ganges and Nile, for the Chinese are singularly unmystical people. The wise, as Confucius had counseled, may have taken delight in their rivers, but since wisdom has alighted on the hands of the Chinese it is the man-made river that figures most in their literature. The delight of the cultivated gentleman is not to stand in a wobbly canoe throwing sticks at marsh fowl, but to sit

257

calmly in a flat-bottomed boat as it floats almost motionless on a canal, noting the play of sunlight filtered through willow branches. For poet and painter, the romantic violence of nature had at times the same attraction that it frequently exercised over the European mind; but for the sage, the scholar who is the most revered type in Chinese thinking, it was the human side of the equation that was meaningful. (PLATE 19)

For many centuries, Chinese and Arab found enough in common for them to bring the two halves of the world into a closer communion than they had known before. They were the last of the great empires on the ancient plan, and both seem to have sensed their distinctiveness as opposed to the barbarians beyond their ken. Both built their civilizations around their rivers, proudly developing a riverine technology inherited from all their predecessors, elements of which went back to the very awakening of human consciousness.

Neither civilization produced any fundamental change in the relationships that had existed between men and their rivers since the rise of the early city-states. Such a change would be made, eventually, by people who had never really had any share in the ancient world community, and whose culture was, in the tenth century, just beginning to assume forms unlike those of any that had preceded it. European civilization would be the first in which industrialization would be possible. But both Arabs and Chinese rejected water power and the industrialized society it would eventually make possible. Perhaps that is why they were able to understand each other, and to deal with each other without any sacrifice of dignity or integrity, in a way that neither could deal with Europe later on. It is certainly why both Arab and Chinese civilizations belonged essentially, for so many centuries, to the ancient world, the world that

258

was inhabited by the Pharaohs, by Chandragupta, by Sennacherib, and Darius, and Wu Ti. That world gave scope for splendor, but no opportunity for the mass of man-kind to free themselves from physical drudgery.

Through Arab civilization, transmitted in bits and pieces to Europe, there is a thread, but only a thread, of continuity between ancient and modern. Perhaps there might have been a genuine continuum if Chinese and Arab had developed water power. But it would have changed their civilization into something they could hardly have recognized and would certainly not have wanted. It is only to-day, after the techniques that have grown from water power have produced a world no man in the tenth century could have dreamed, that Asia and Africa have desired to share a technology which can once again draw the whole world of man into community.

CHAPTER XI

The Glory That Was

ON THE map of the human adventure, the period round
about the tenth century of the Christian reckoning appears
to be one of the watersheds. Looking back at it today, we
can see that men had come near a place at which the
streams of human energy would divide, some flowing back
over territory long familiar and some spilling over into new
channels that would lead towards unsuspected destinies.
A thousand years earlier the human mind had reached that
particular crest: Vitruvius had described it and Antipater
had shouted that it led towards new freedoms. But although the discovery of water power is the crucial event,
human history did not begin to move in a new direction
until water power was widely used and applied to a variety
of industrial tasks. These developments began, on a significant scale, only in the centuries following the tenth; even
then, they did not occur in the centers of ancient culture
but far out on the fringes, in Europe, where people were
building a new and different civilization.

In some ways, the advent of water power means more to us today than any of the great dividing lines over which humanity has marched in the past. Although we know it is only one of many events which have altered the whole composition of human society and have redirected its energies, yet it seems somehow a boundary more distinct than that which separates the food-producing barbarian from the food-gathering savage, or the city-dwelling non-producer from both. One reason is simply that it is nearer to us in time, and another is that we still live in the world it initiated. But this alone is not enough to make it tower up, as it does, like a continental divide between us and all that is ancient and alien.

The average person who was alive at the time of, say, the Roman domination was actually closer in his spiritual outlook to men who had been dead for thousands of years than to the average person who lives in the twentieth century. Like the cave-dwelling hunters, and the first farmers, and the people who lived in Ur or Mohenjo-Daro, he knew that most of the enormous drudgery which was essential for his very existence had to be done by muscles, either his own or those of another human being. Rivers could sustain heavy burdens and winds could move them, and a certain amount of pulling and hauling could be done by animals; but for all the day-to-day lifting and grinding and digging and cutting, the mining and the hoeing, the harvesting and the building, there was literally no usable power except the strength of arms and legs and backs. Neither coal nor petroleum had been discovered; the only fuel was wood or dung, whose burning produced energy only in the form of heat, and no one could convert that heat into useful work.

Yet all the way along, from the caves to the towered cities, the need for power had steadily increased. One of the paradoxes in the story of men's effort to control their environment is that at each advance towards the goal a larger amount of physical work became necessary for the survival of the race. Although the work energy in the human body is very small, it was enough to sustain man in a hunting society. A family group could, by their own physical efforts, collect enough food and simple tools to survive; they could even make themselves rich and respected, according to the standards of their society. But in higher stages of social development, as luxuries became necessities, men found that it took more effort to keep alive. The production of food made humanity safer and richer than it had been before, but it also bound the individual to the performance of more, and more continuous, physical exertion. To find a comfortable cave and to locate the game herds requires only a fraction of the effort that men must expend when they build houses, feed and care for tamed animals, and tend cultivated fields.

In the early stages of the agricultural revolution, much of the extra muscle power that was needed was furnished by the newly domesticated animals. As development proceeded, however, the supply of power could not keep up with the demand. The use of metals, for example, gave men greater strength and more control over nature, but in return the tasks of mining, smelting, and fashioning exacted an enormous amount of work energy which had not been required before. So did the building of cities, with their temples and their gigantic monuments, and so did the construction of roads, harbors, bridges, canals, dams, and aqueducts. When the need for power outran the supply that could possibly be extracted from animals and from the spontaneous labor of free individuals, there was only one other possible source. The energy in human muscles had to be dragooned; human beings, in ever-increasing numbers, had to be enslaved, stripped of everything that made them human, and forced to become mere laboring animals. This was necessary in order that some few individuals, a smaller and smaller percentage of the whole mass of humanity, might be relatively free.

This necessity for slavery, this being constantly surrounded by masses of creatures who looked like human beings but were not, this nagging fear that one might at any moment be enslaved himself, troubled all the enlightened minority among the free. They did not talk much about it; they tried not to think about it; but it pervades all they did and all they recorded, giving it a queer, inhuman twist that is alien to the modern mind. The Egyptian officer, reporting to his superiors that "he" had dug fifteen wells near the stone quarry, thriftily adds that he got the necessary manpower at the bargain rate: "to each [slave] . . . two jars of water and twenty loaves daily," much as a modern engineer might report that for the expenditure of so many gallons of gasoline he drilled so many feet into the earth. As time went on, the thinking part of mankind grew less and less happy about their dependence on slaves, but they could think of no way to free themselves of it.

Aristotle, pondering the bleak question of morality in a slave society, could find no way out of the dilemma. Platonic ideals of a Republic of Man, in which human beings could give their energies to the kind of joyful creative activity for which they seem fitted, were all very well and good, but the drudgery would have to be done by slaves, for the simple reason that no free man could submit to it and remain free. At that point in his thinking, the mind of Aristotle suddenly leaped forward over the centuries to the only possible alternative: "If machines could move of themselves, as the fable says the tripods of Hephaestus picked themselves up and removed to another place . . ." That was the solution, and the only one. But then he admitted the shattering fact: "This is impossible."

For his generation, and for some fifteen hundred years after him, it was. And it is this, more than anything else, that makes the ancient world so alien to us. Millions of people, of course, still live in societies where mechanical energy is not yet widely used, and several million are still actual slaves, but there is hardly a human being alive today who does not know that body- and soul-destroying drudgery is no longer necessary. If we find it difficult to enter into the mind of one who lived before the advent of water power, it is primarily because we, who are each served by mechanical power equal to that of many scores of slaves, can hardly imagine ourselves attended by a host of human beings whom slavery has changed into dumb beasts of burden. And of course to conceive a world in which we ourselves would belong to the enormous majority of ancient mankind is completely beyond us. We can sometimes comprehend the wars and the plagues and the fun of the river carnivals; we can admire the carvings and be awed by the pyramids and aqueducts; we even think we can understand the weird religions and find values in the pitifully inadequate philosophies. But always we come up finally against the terrifying realities of a world in which machines could not move of themselves.

Nevertheless, our roots are in that world. It not only contained the whole of human experience up to a thousand years ago; it produced many of the elements that would eventually be fused into the instruments we would use to break down its oppressive walls. In the control and use of rivers, which have played such a vital role in the creation of the modern world and which offer even more promise for our development in the immediate future, men in the muscle-powered societies made virtually all the basic discoveries from which we profit.

Rivers are very nearly the most powerful and awe-inspiring of all natural forces; next to the sun, as the ancient Egyptians intuitively realized, they are the one on which we, by our very nature, are dependent. It is no wonder that men at certain stages of their development have fallen on their faces before the rivers in terror and adoration, worshiping them as gods. But far more wonderful is the matter-of-fact way in which from the earliest periods they set about using them, not only as sources of water for drinking and bathing but as hunting grounds for a basic food. The impact that the discovery of fishing made on the minds of men is still felt. When it was new, men were so overwhelmed by it that the fish itself was deified, and even today millions of us acknowledge the awe we still feel at one of men's greatest discoveries by the potency of the symbolism we attach to fish, and by the veneration with which we eat its flesh on occasions of penance and purification.

But men of the ancient world went far beyond the mere use of the river and its products. They undertook to control it, to lead its waters out of their natural channels, to push them back from fields they wanted to cultivate, to make it help in the creation of the kind of environment they wanted to live in. It was not easy, and the rivers often broke through the barricades, but men persisted until they had learned nearly all we know today about flood control except the role of plants and trees. There are not many details, actually, in the construction of waterworks which men did not discover before they had mechanical power to help with the physical labor. To take only one example in addition to those cited earlier in this book, in the Grand

Anicut, a dam 1,080 feet long built across the Coleroon River in ancient India,

> part of the crest was designed to the same smooth curve (engineers call it an 'ogee curve') which modern designers use for spillways. And the downstream toe of the anicut was prudently protected from undermining by a long apron of stone. In 1830, the first British engineers to tackle the problem of irrigation from the delta of a major river came upon that Grand Anicut in Tanjore. . . . It taught [one of them, Captain Arthur Cotton] what no living engineer or treatise then affirmed: that dams capable of withstanding the full force of the river at its mouth could be founded not on rock, but on pure sand. Captain Cotton risked his reputation and his career on that revolutionary demonstration. He built the Upper Anicut across the Coleroon by the same technique. And when he had proved that the feat of the Chola kings could be reproduced by engineering science, he got authority to dam the Godavari and the Krishna and the Mahanadi. Every one of those great barriers, resting safely on sand, is a monument to ancient engineering and modern ability to learn. (Hart: *New India's Rivers*, p. 17.)

By the time of Christ, the consciousness which had awakened in the early fire makers had made what is still, perhaps, the most significant discovery in all its long effort to make men capable of controlling their own destinies. Machines were invented which could be moved by the force of water as it flowed on its witless way towards the sea.

The culmination of the development this discovery set in motion could not be reached, of course, until men had learned a great number of things they did not know about the river and its ways, and a great many about man himself, his nature and the possibilities in his social activity. All these would have to be found out one by one, studied and sorted and eventually fitted into the synthesis of thought and action which we call "whole-basin development." But the vital element, the knowledge that inanimate force could be made to work for men, was already there, waiting to be fully used.

Certain other ideas that are fundamental to modern river use were also known in the ancient world. In the conscious use of one project to serve more than one purpose, for example, there is the same kind of two-birds-with-one-stone philosophy that prompts the modern engineer to think almost exclusively in terms of multipurpose dams. In his plans for using the Habbaniya depression, Alexander was certainly thinking of both flood control and improvement of navigation; and although the needs of Chinese peasants for both flood control and irrigation were usually subordinated by the bureaucrats to the need for moving the grain tribute, all three were certainly present in the emperors' minds. When Rome finally began to grind her grain by water mills, she supplied them with water from the same aqueducts that brought her the means of keeping clean and slaking her thirst. Again, in the concern for controlling silt deposition and using it constructively, there is an inkling of modern concepts. There was even some understanding of the river's role in maintaining human health; one sees it not only in the use of streams as healing agents but in some measures for public action against contamination from polluted water. The Romans did not realize the deadly menace of the mosquito, and they never actually drained the Pontine marshes, but many of them knew that those marshes ought to be drained, simply because they were a nuisance.

What was missing was, of course, a synthesis of all the bits and pieces of knowledge about rivers which they had, a perception of relationships. As a result, there is always something piecemeal and isolated about the river-control and water-conservancy projects of antiquity. They built gigantic and eminently useful structures, they connected disparate streams by canals, but they never seem to have understood the relationship between what was done at one point along a river's bank and what might be done anywhere else. Though they explored certain rivers from their mouths right up to their ultimate sources, they never grasped the concept of the river as an indivisible unit, a living organism intimately related throughout all its parts. On extremely few rivers did they ever attempt more than one dam. As for the concept of development of the basin as a whole, there was scarcely an inkling. Strabo may have realized something of the basin's significance as a geographic entity, but of its possibility as a field for planned social engineering, no engineer could conceive. These observations in no way belittle the achievements of ancient men, which were enormous; with all the advantages of mechanical power to help us, such ideas did not occur to anybody until the beginning of the twentieth century.

There were moments, however, in which there seemed to be a glimpse of the distant future. Sometimes when men dreamed, and told their dreams in myth, it seems as if they were striving to establish, through illusion, relationships of control over their rivers which, because of scanty technology, they could not achieve in fact. A good example is the story of how Hercules won his wife, Deianira, by wrestling with his rival, the god of the river Achelous. In Ovid's lively version, the river-god's account of the battle is a remarkable summary of the various steps an engineer might take in a struggle to subdue a river.

The first encounter is indecisive: expecting an easy victory, the man lashes out blindly, seeming to think he can seize the river's body at any point and easily pin it down.

> He caught up dust and sprinkled me, and I likewise
>   with sands
> Made him all yellow too. One while he at my neck
>   doth snatch,
> Another while my clear, crisp legs he striveth for to
>   catch,
> Or trips at me, and everywhere the 'vantage he doth
>   watch.
> My weightiness defended me, and clearly did defeat
> His stout assaults. . . .[1]

This random snatching and grabbing gets Hercules nowhere; panting, he backs away to take the measure of this unexpectedly dangerous and slippery antagonist. Then in the hope of conquering by main force, he tries the attack direct, hurling himself on the middle body of the river. "Methought a mountain whelmed me," Achelous confesses, but with a mighty effort he breaks through this dam —not, however, before Hercules has got another hold on him farther upstream:

> . . . He following still his 'vantage, suffered not
> Me once to breathe or gather strength, but by and
>   by he got
> Me by the neck. Then was I fain to sink with knee
>   to ground
> And kiss the dust. Now when in strength too weak
>   myself I found
> I took me to my sleights and slipped in shape of snake
>   away

[1] *Metamorphoses*, tr. Golding, Everyman's Library, p. 295.

Of wondrous length; and when that I of purpose him
    to fray
Did bend myself in swelling rolls, and made a hideous
    noise
Of hissing with my forked tongue, he smiling at my
    toys
And laughing them to scorn, said thus: "It is my cradle
    game
To vanquish snakes, O Achelous."[2]

On the meandering upper courses of the twisting river,
the battle goes on, until finally

. . . his fingers of my neck he fastened in the nape.
Methought he graned my throat as though he did
    with pincers nip.[3]

At this point, where the two main tributaries of the actual
river Achelous curve down like a pair of horns into the
main stream, the river-god tries his last trick:

I turning to the shape of bull rebelled against my foe.
He stepping to my left side close did fold his arms
    about
My wattled neck, and following me then running
    mainly out,
Did drag me back and made me pitch my horns
    against the ground,
And in the deepest of the sand he overthrew me
    round.
And yet not so content, such hold his cruel hand did
    take
Upon my welked horn that he asunder quite it brake,
And pulled it from my maimed brow.[4]

[2] *Idem*, pp. 295–6.
[3] *Idem*
[4] *Idem*, pp. 296–7.

This myth was clearly conceived by some poet who had thought seriously, and with a great deal of penetration, about the problems of hydraulic engineering. He also knew the rich rewards that would follow successful river control, for he tells how, as soon as the left fork of the stream is wrenched off from the main body, water sprites snatch the horn up to heaven where it is turned into a cornucopia, pouring out a wealth of fruit and flowers upon the reclaimed valley and enriching the whole kingdom through which the river flows.

The myth of Hercules' conquest of the river Achelous gives us almost our only hint in ancient literature that men in the period of the world empires had begun to dream of river control exercised over an entire basin. Only in our own generation has such complete valley development been realized in practice, as engineers working on many rivers throughout the world have built a whole series of installations, all integrated into a "TVA" system for controlling and using the water all the way from the source to the mouth. The "basin-concept" is a contemporary achievement, but the dream that it might be done seems to have been in human minds for over two thousand years.

There is even one myth that anticipates the most subtle conception in our modern programs for complete water-and-land conservation in the development of a river valley and the fullest use of its resources. Afforestation of the watershed, in order to build up the soil and prevent both erosion on the hills and floods in the valleys, has only recently been recognized by engineers as an element in whole-basin projects just as essential as dams and penstocks. But in the ancient myth of Erysichthon the danger and the wickedness of deforestation was recognized, and the story of his gruesome fate was told as a solemn warning. Erysichthon was a willful and impious man, who as a gesture of sheer defiance of the gods cut down a grove that was sacred to Demeter, the Greek goddess of vegetation. His servants warned him of the danger, especially when blood began to gush from the wounded tree trunks and the nymphs within them cried aloud in pain. But the willful man seized an axe himself and hacked at a great oak until he brought it to the ground. Demeter in fury called upon Famine to avenge her; this hideous hag breathed herself into Erysichthon's body as he lay sleeping after his exertions, and he awoke in a frenzy of hunger. His insatiable craving for food caused him to strip his whole kingdom, dissipating the wealth his father had bequeathed him and leaving the land barren and its people destitute. When he had sold his own daughter into prostitution for food and was still starving, in the final extremity of famine,

> Most cursed caitiff as he was, with biting he did rend
> His flesh, and by diminishing his body did intend
> To feed his body, till that death did speed his fatal
>   end.[5]

It is significant that Ovid pairs this story with that of the conquering of Achelous, seeming to underline the famine that follows on deforestation by the contrast with the horn of plenty which pours out its riches on a valley properly developed.

But that men should imitate Hercules was out of the question. The earth cannot be really used for the good of men until all men are able to use their part of it in dignity and freedom. That is the principal thing we have learned in the last thousand years. We have not yet achieved it, but from the use of the river's power we have gone on to discover other sources of energy, until we have become

5 *Idem*, p. 293.

giants who can contend with nature on a more than equal footing. That power has enabled us to free ourselves from drudgery and poverty and contempt. It has prepared us to set about the building of a world in which no human being need be ashamed, or afraid, to live.

The fact that the use of mechanical power did not exist in earlier ages may be the chief reason why men did not achieve that other goal of human striving: the creation of some kind of world community, in which all could participate equally. What their experience did prove is that community cannot be imposed by force. When men are driven by whips to the performance of mighty deeds, they lose the humanity that makes them capable of co-operation. Neither Egyptians, Mesopotamians, Persians, Greeks, Romans, Indians, Chinese, or Arabs, though they were all led at times by men as efficient and gifted as any who ever lived, were able to solve the dilemma of imperialism. They explored nearly all its possibilities and proved that all its roads led to dead ends.

But in their work with rivers, they gave us clues that may prove to be among the most effective tools we have for building a society in which the twin goals may be attainable. Rivers, and the relationships men have established with them, have lain at the heart of the human adventure through all the centuries. In the tenth century, the use of their enormous potential had only begun.

SOME SUGGESTIONS FOR
FURTHER READING

On the assumption that the reader may want some suggestions for further and more detailed reading, rather than an exhaustive list of all the works I have consulted in preparing this book, I have thought it best to offer a sampling of enjoyable and informative books in which various aspects of men's relations with rivers, at different times and in different places, are discussed from a variety of points of view. Few are concerned exclusively with rivers, but I think the general reader will find most of them more interesting and helpful than technical treatises.

Chi Ch'ao-Ting: *Key Economic Areas in Chinese History, as Revealed in the Development of Works for Water-Control*, New York and London, 1936.

Childe, V. Gordon: *Man Makes Himself*, London, 1936.

———: *New Light on the Most Ancient East*, London, 1934.

Clark, John Graham Douglas: *Prehistoric Europe, the Economic Basis*, New York, 1952.

Drower, M. S.: chapter on "Water Supply, Irrigation, and Agriculture," *A History of Technology*, ed. Singer, Holmyard, and Hall, vol. 1, Oxford, 1954.

Encyclopedia of Religion and Ethics: article on "Water and Water Gods."

Forbes, R. J.: chapters on "Power" and "Water Engineering and Sanitation," *A History of Technology*, vol. 2, Oxford, 1956.

———: *Man the Maker*, New York, 1950.

Frankfort, Henri: *The Art and Architecture of the Ancient Orient*, Pelican History of Art, London, 1954.

—————— et. al.: *Before Philosophy*, Penguin (originally published as *The Intellectual Adventure of Ancient Man*, Chicago, 1946).

Frontinus, Sextus Julius: *The Aqueducts of Rome*, translated by Charles E. Bennett, Loeb Classical Library, 1925.

The Geography of Strabo, translated by Horace L. Jones, Loeb Classical Library, 1917 *et seq.*

Ghirshman, R.: *Iran*, Penguin, 1954.

Glueck, Nelson: *The River Jordan*, Philadelphia, 1946.

Hart, Henry C.: *New India's Rivers*, Bombay, 1956.

Herodotus: *The Histories*, translated by Aubrey de Selincourt, Penguin, 1954.

Hitti, Philip: *History of the Arabs*, London, 1946.

——————: *History of Syria*, New York, 1951.

Hornell, James: *Water Transport: Origins and Early Evolution*, Cambridge, 1946.

Hourani, George F.: *Arab Seafaring in the Indian Ocean*, Princeton, 1951.

Levy, Reuben: *A Baghdad Chronicle*, Cambridge, 1929.

Lewis, Bernard: *The Arabs in History*, London, 1950.

Lloyd, Seton: *Twin Rivers*, Bombay, 1943.

Ludwig, Emil: *The Nile, the life-story of a river*, New York, 1937.

Majumdar, R. C., Raychaudhuri, H. C., and Datta, Kalikinkar: *An Advanced History of India*, London, 1946.

Needham, Joseph: *Science and Civilisation in China*, Cambridge, 1954–

Robins, F. W.: *The Story of Water Supply*, Oxford, 1946.

Thomson, George: *Studies in Ancient Greek Society*, London, 1949.

Thomson, J. Oliver: *History of Ancient Geography*, Cambridge, 1948.

Toynbee, Arnold: *A Study of History*, especially vol. 2, London, 1934 ff.

Usher, Abbott Payson: *A History of Mechanical Inventions*, rev. ed., Harvard, 1954.

Vitruvius on Architecture, translated by Frank Granger, Loeb Classical Library, 1931.

Wheeler, Sir Mortimer: *The Indus Civilization*, Cambridge, 1954.

————: *Rome Beyond the Imperial Frontiers*, Penguin, 1954.

Wright, J. K.: *Geographical Lore in the Time of the Crusades*, New York, 1925.

Xenophon: *The Persian Expedition*, translated by Rex Warner, Penguin, 1949.

Abbasids, 242, 243, 251
Abd al-Rahman III, 243
Abyssinia, 56
Achaemenians, 144, 154, 155, 158, 183
Achelous R., 216, 268, 270, 271, 272
Achilles, 118, 136
Actium, 162
Aden and Aden Gulf, 162, 166
Adonis, River of, 86
Aegean, 201
Aesculapius, 137
afforestation, 271
Afghanistan, 147
Africa, 44, 52, 57, 74, 134, 151, 162, 203, 248
  See also North Africa
agora, 233
agricultural revolution, 53, 74, 113, 262
Agriculture, 182
Agrippa, Marcus, 195
Ahuramazda, 154
Ain Musa, 86
Akhenaton, 139
Akkad, 93, 130, 133, 243
Akkadia, 99, 128
Akki, 134
Alexander, 155, 157, 158, 162, 181, 187, 225, 267
Alexandria, 161, 162, 204, 226, 241
Algeria, 184
Algonquin Indians, 119
Allegheny R., 25
Alpheios R., 136
Amanus range, 99
Amazon R., 22, 51
Amenemhet I, quoted 89
Ames, Russell, 7
Amestris, 120
Amon, 125
Amr ibn-al-As, 241
Amu Darya R., 144
Anigros R., 136
animals, 39, 40, 41, 43, 48, 50, 51, 55, 98, 99

domestication of, 45, 53, 54, 80, 262
Anti-Lebanon, 84
Antipater, 231, 260
Antoninus, Marcus Aurelius, 170
Antony, Mark, 193
Apamea, 229
Aphrodite, 129
Appian Way, 194
Apsu, 126
aqueducts, 83, 87, 109, 111, 180, 187, 194, 195, 196, 233, 242, 243, 245, 262, 264, 267
Arabia and Arabs, 83, 93, 95, 132, 147, 151, 152, 158, 160, 162, 163, 165, 172, 174, 184, 197, 237, 238–248, 273
Arabian Sea, 186
Arab-China contact, 248–259
Arab language, 242, 247
Arachosians, 147
Arad-Ea, 131
Aral Sea, 26, 148
Aramaic language, 154, 156, 247
Archimedes, 226, 229
Arctic Ocean, 26, 57
Arethusa, 133
Aristobulos, 181, 214
Aristotle, 211, 212, 216, quoted 263–264
Arles, 233
Armenia, 88, 99, 105, 203
Artaxerxes Mnemon, 202
Artemis, 133
artificial lakes, 95, 96, 102, 243
Ashanti, 134
Ashur-bani-pal, 110
Asia, 51, 52, 160, 169, 172, 187
Asia Minor, 100, 143, 150, 151, 152, 154, 158, 165, 196
  See also Central Asia
Asoka, 186
Assyria and Assyrians, 90, 92, 95, 97, 108, 109, 111, 112, 128, 144, 147, 210
Aswan, 95
Athens, 75, 148, 195, 233

Atlantic Ocean, 23, 56, 57
Atlantis, 23
Attica, 150
Augustus, 162, 195
Avicenna, 247
Azov, Sea of, 216
Azupirani, 134

Baal, 124
Babel, Tower of, 127, 154
Babylon and Babylonia, 36, 64, 87–
    88, 93, 97, 98, 100, 101, 105,
    109, 110, 111, 114, 116, 126,
    128, 135, 142, 147, 150, 153,
    157, 225, 243, 244
Bacton, 181
Bactria and Bactrians, 148, 164,
    169, 251
Badagas, 135
Baghdad, 104, 243, 244, 247
Barada R., 85, 87, 241
basin concept. See whole basin
bathing and baths, 85, 183, 252,
    265, 267
Batu Kahn, 104
bellows, 232, 254, 255
Benares, 124
Bengal, 123
Béni-Abbès, 184
Bitter Lakes, 152
Black Sea, 132, 151, 157, 158, 161,
    174, 201, 202, 216
boats, 44, 46, 47, 70, 71, 72, 76, 82,
    96, 98, 113, 131, 138, 187, 244
Bokhara, 245
Bosphorus, 151, 178, 180
Brahmaputra R., 167, 170, 238
"breast wheel," 255
Breuil, Abbé, 40
bridges, 96, 105, 177, 178, 180, 236,
    243, 247, 262
Britain, 23, 82, 203
Brittain, Mary Zwemer, 7
Brittain, Robert, quoted 196–197
Bronze Age, 29
Buddhism, 154, 172
Burma, 159, 167
Busumakwe lake, 134
Byblos, 86, 153

Byzantium, 172, 173, 181, 196, 197,
    228, 237

Caecus, Appius Claudius. See
    Claudius
Caesar, 104, 177
Cairo, 77, 241, 245
calendar, 77, 78
California, 62
Caligula, 195
canals, 62, 64, 82, 87, 90, 93–94,
    101, 108, 109, 110, 129, 152,
    157, 159, 161, 170, 185, 187,
    189, 190, 191, 192, 196, 198,
    199, 216, 217, 226, 227, 236,
    237, 241, 243, 245, 250, 262
"Canals, Diggers of," 91
Canton, 249
Cappadocia, 147
caravan routes and caravans, 99,
    143, 153, 159, 161, 165, 201,
    244, 249
Carchemish, 153
Carlsbad Caverns, 196
Carthage, 193, 195, 196
Caryanda, 152
Caspian Sea, 26, 132, 148, 160, 165,
    168, 174, 201, 204
Cato, 193
Caucasus, 161, 165, 168
Cauvery R., 167
cave dwellers and caves, 33, 35, 37,
    39, 40, 48, 50, 123, 133, 197,
    261, 262
Cavendish, Henry, 48
Central Asia, 97, 132, 156, 159, 160,
    167, 168, 172, 174, 184, 201,
    203, 238, 249
Centrites R., 105, 120
Ceylon, 159, 186
chain-of-buckets, 225, 228
Chaldees, 87
Chandragupta Maurya, 159, 185,
    186, 259
Chang-an, 249, 251
Chang Ch'ien, 163, 164
Chang Jung, quoted 217
Charon, 131
Cheng Kuo, 189

Chengtu, 189, 199
Cheops, 70, 126
Chiang R., 207
Childe, V. Gordon, 68, *quoted* 80, 274
Ch'in, 189, 192
China and Chinese, 24, 66, 88, 104, 155, 163–165, 169, 170, 171, 172, 174, 182, 184, 187–193, 199, 205–211, 232, 237, 273
-Arab contacts, 248–259
Chinese People's Republic, 251
Ching R., 189
Chirisophus, 120
Choaspes R., 87, 103, 147
Chorasmians, 148
Chosroes I, 236, 237, 240
Christianity, 240
circulation of waters, 211–212
cisterns, 94, 108, 111, 195, 196, 220, 234, 245
cities and city-states, 80–88, 99, 100, 107–111, 127, 143, 148, 151, 258, 261, 262
Clark, F. LeGros, 7
Claudius, Appius Caecus, 194, 195
Cleopatra, 161–162, 165
climate, 43, 170, 187, 248
coinage, 149, 154–155
Coleroon R., 266
Columbus, Christopher, 152, 159
commerce. *See* trade
Confucius, *quoted* 137, 155, 257
Congo, 22
conservation, 246, 271
See also water conservancy
Constantine, 233
Constantinople, 171–172, 173, 198
co-operation, 30, 31, 45, 49, 72, 73, 75, 107, 246, 273
Cordova, 242, 243, 245
cotton, 112, 159, 165, 167, 243
creation, 64, 78, 123, 188
Croesus, 105, 149
Ctesias, 202
Ctesibius, 226
Ctesiphon, 170, 243
cultivating, 56, 60, 63, 73, 79, 81, 262, 265

See also farming
Cyprus, 216
Cyrus, 87, 101, 102, 106, 116, 118, 144, 149
Cyrus R., 161, 168

Damanu canal, 94
Damascus, 84, 85, 86, 241
dams, 30, 53–79, 83, 92, 93, 101, 106, 111, 127, 183, 185, 186, 188, 197, 235, 236, 237, 238, 239, 245, 262, 266, 267, 268
Danube, 104, 144, 148, 151, 178, 202, 240
Dardanelles, 151, 161
Darius, 144, 147, *quoted* 148, 149, 151, 152, 155, 156, 160, 161, 165, 169, 177, 184, 236, 247, 259
inscriptions, 141–142, 145–146
Dead Sea, 21
deforestation, 271–272
Deianira, 268
Deinocrates, 181
Delphi, 101
deltas, 23, 24, 27, 28, 64, 78, 86, 123, 157, 188, 215, 216
Demeter, 272
Denmark, 44, 49
de Lesseps, F., 162, 247
de Selincourt, Aubrey, 88
"devil-worshipers," 135
"dew mounds," 197
Diades, 181
"Diggers of Canals," 91
dikes, 66, 90, 107, 185, 188, 189, 191, 207, 216, 237, 238
Diodorus Siculus, 96
Diognetos, 181
Disraeli, Benjamin, 162
ditches, 53–79, 74, 82, 103, 105, 107, 183, 187, 220, 224
Diyala R., 244
Don, 104, 148, 204, 216
Dordogne R., 40
drainage, 22, 47, 62, 65, 74, 79, 82, 94, 106, 130, 187, 188, 291, 241
dredging, 216, 217

drinking water, 34, 83, 102, 108, 129, 166, 220, 265
drought, 30, 185
Drower, M. S., 7, 108, *quoted* 112, 127, 274
Druids, 124
Dryas R., 132
"dry zone," 186–187
Dyris R., 212

Ea, 126, 127, 128, 136
Ecbatana, 147, 153
Edessa, 235
Egypt and Egyptians, 24, 46, 55, 58, 59, 62, 63, 64, 65, 68, 69, 70, 74, 85, 87, 90, 91, 92, 94, 97, 98, 106, 111, 122, 124, 125, 126, 130, 132, 143, 147, 150, 152, 158, 160, 161, 166, 180, 183, 184, 201, 202, 226, 235, 265, 273
Elam, 147
Elis, 133
Elisha, 85, *quoted* 103
empire building and empires, 99, 104, 106, 114, 116, 130, 143, 146, 147, 152, 154, 158, 160, 163–168, 169, 170, 175–199
engineering and engineers, 175–199, 245, 263, 271
England, 23, 47, 62, 66, 124
Enlil, 128
Erbil, 110, 183
Eridu, 127
erosion, 215, 271
Erysichthon, 271, 272
Esarhaddon, *quoted* 111, 142
Esdraelon, 63
Ethiopia, 147, 150, 203
Eudoxus, 162, 163
Eupalinus, 180
Euphrates, 24, 36, 54, 58, 63, 74, 80, 87, 88, 93, 95, 96, 98, 102, 105, 111, 126, 128, 131, 134, 136, 139, 142, 144, 153, 157, 162, 165, 170, 172, 238, 243
Europe and Europeans, 23, 37, 38, 39, 42, 43, 44, 51, 57, 74, 82, 97, 105, 117, 150, 160, 162, 171, 203, 241, 248, 260
Euxine Sea, 203

Fa-Hien, 172
Famine, 272
farmers and farming, 57, 58, 67, 69, 72, 79, 81, 106, 108, 150, 185, 215, 216, 217, 221, 227, 254, 261
Fayum depression, 58
Ferghana, 165, 168
fertility, 125, 126, 130, 136
fire, 48, 267
fish and fishing, 40–43, 44, 50, 51, 53, 54, 55, 60, 73, 82, 106, 121, 125, 135, 138, 150, 187, 214, 219, 244, 247, 257, 265
floating mills, 252
floats, 104, 105, 177
flood and floods, 37, 56, 59, 63, 64, 66, 77, 86, 91, 92, 101, 106, 108, 110, 128, 182, 185, 186, 191, 198, 237, 238, 247
control, 64, 183, 257, 265, 267
warnings, 107
food gathering, 34, 36, 37, 38, 41, 42, 47, 51, 52, 54, 60, 73, 261, 262
food production, 52, 54, 55, 57, 69, 73, 74, 82, 106, 143, 255, 261, 262
force pump, 226
fords, 105, 120, 121, 177
Formosa, 249
foundlings, 133
France, 39, 48, 195, 233
Frankfort, Henri, 70, *quoted* 129–130, *quoted* 145–146, 210, 275
freedom, 47, 61, 77, 272, 273
Frontinus, Sextus Julius, 194, *quoted* 196, 275
Fukien, 190

Ganga, 123
Ganges, 24, 123, 124, 138, 159, 167, 169, 170, 201, 238, 248, 257
Gates of Hercules, 203
Gauls, 195

Geneva, Lake of, 22
Genghis Khan, 104
geographical concepts, 34–35, 200–218, 248
Ghirshman, *quoted* 141–142, 150, *quoted* 153, 275
Ghutah, 241
Gilgit, 164
Girnar, 186, 238
glaciers, 26, 27, 38
Goethals, G. W., 62
"Golden Horde," 104
Gorgos, 181
Goths, 237
grain grinding and mills, 220, 224, 225, 254, 255, 267
grain tribute, 151, 190–191, 217, 249, 257, 267
Grand Anicut, 266
Grand Canal (China), 193, 250
Greater Zab R., 109
Great Lakes, 25
"Great Mother," 128
Great Pyramid, 70
Greece and Greeks, 74, 86, 103, 105, 120, 131, 135, 148, 150, 151, 155, 157, 158, 161, 177, 180, 201, 225, 231, 273
Greek language, 247
grindstone, 220, 224, 229
Guadalquivir R., 243, 245
Gulf of Corinth, 216
Gulf of Mexico, 24, 25, 91
Guptas, 172, 186, 238
Gutians, 114
Gyndus, 116

Habbaniya depression, 267
Hadhramaut, 239
Hadrian, 195, *quoted* 201
Halys R., 105, 149
Hama, 229
Hamadan, 147
Hammurabi and Hammurabi's Code, *quoted* 90–91, *quoted* 94, 135, 179, 213, 241, 246
Han Chi, 254, 255
Handel, George Frederick, 139

Han dynasty, 163, 170, 190, 192, 199, 207, 208, 254, 255
hanging gardens, 111, 142, 225
Hanno, 203
Hapi, 124–125
Harappa, 85
Harpagus, 101
Hart, Henry C., *quoted* 266, 275
Harun-al-Rashid, 243, 244, 247
Hatshepsut, 112
health, 38, 267
    See also public health
Heber, Reginald, 124
Hecataeus, 201
Hellespont, 117, 118, 119, 178
Heraclitus, *quoted* 137
Hercules, 132, 268, 269, 271, 272
    Gates of, 203
Herodotus, *quoted* 55, *quoted* 87–88, 92, *quoted* 95, *quoted* 96, 98, *quoted* 101, 104, *quoted* 117, *quoted* 118, 119, *quoted* 120, 135, *quoted* 177, *quoted* 178–179, 201, 205, 214, 215, 225, 244
Hezekiah, 102
Himalaya, 123
Himalayas, 24, 26, 28
Hindu Kush, 147, 159, 160
Hippalus, 166
Ho R., 207
    See also Yellow River
Holland and Hollanders, 66, 165
Homer, 119
horizontal water wheel, 256, 257
Hornell, James, 98, *quoted* 134–135, 275
Hsu Hsia-Kuo, 209
Huai R., 188, 191, 192, 257
Huan, 188
Huang Ti, 206, 207
Hudson R., 96
hunters and hunting, 33, 34, 35, 37, 39–41, 44, 58, 60, 67, 72, 77, 79, 81, 83, 166, 187, 261, 262, 265
Huxley, Julian, *quoted* 93
Hwang Ho, 24, 58, 170, 188
    See also Yellow River

281

Ice Ages, 25, 26, 37, 39, 57
Idrisi, 248
Illinois R., 25
Imperial Valley (Calif.), 62
Incas, 97, 160
India and Indians, 24, 72, 74, 121, 135, 150, 152, 155, 156, 157, 159, 160 162, 164, 165, 166, 168, 169, 170, 172, 182, 185, 186, 201, 203, 214–215, 229, 233, 238, 239, 249, 266, 273
Indiana, 25
Indian Ocean, 52, 166, 167
Indo-China, 190
Indus, 27, 58, 80, 85, 87, 88, 94, 132, 144, 151, 152, 155, 158, 159, 160, 164, 167, 170, 183, 184, 201, 214
industrialization, 246, 253, 255, 257, 258, 260
Industrial Revolution, 29
Institute of Saharan Research, 184
international trade, 142–147, 176, 237
   See also trade
Iran, 64, 146, 158, 165, 184
Iraq, 24, 85, 241, 248
Irrawaddy, 20, 170
irrigation, 26, 49, 62, 64, 65, 67, 68, 75, 82, 90, 94, 106, 114, 124, 126, 130, 159, 166, 180, 182, 183, 185, 186, 187, 188, 189, 191, 197, 198, 202, 217, 219, 220, 226, 236, 239, 241, 243, 252, 257, 267
   See also tank irrigation
Ishtar, 110, 129, 134
Isis, 70
Israel, 102, 197
Istanbul, 195, 198
Italy, 196

Jaffe, Elsbeth, 7
Jaghjagh R., 175
Jainism, 154
Jaxartes R. (later Syr Darya), 132, 150, 155, 158, 164, 203, 245, 249
Jehoram, 102

Jehoshaphat, 102
Jericho, 85
Jerusalem, 87, 102
Jerwan, 109
Jordan, 21, 131, 143, 144
Jovian, 177
Judah, 102
Judaism, 154, 240
Judea, 87
Justinian, 173, 177, 198, 236, 237

Kabul R., 147, 151, 153, 156, 164
Kafur R., 147
Karun R., 235, 242
Kashgar, 156, 164, 170
Kesslerloch, 34
Khalid, *quoted* 241
Kharga, 184
Khosr R., 111
Khosru, 236
King of Edom, 102
King Hezekiah, 102
King Himalaya, 123
King of Lydia, 105
King of Nubia, 91
King Santanu, 123
kings and kingship, 81, 89–95, 99, 100, 102, 106, 107, 113, 129, 130, 149, 179
Koran, *quoted* 240, 245
Kuangsi, 190
Kuangtung, 190
Kublai Khan, 210
Kunlun Mountains, 164
Kur, 127
Kurdish hills, 99
Kushan, 164

labor shortage, 233
Lagash, 89
Lake Geneva, 22
Lake Habbaniya, 157
Lake Homs, 83, 93
Lake Maeotis, 216
Lake Sudarsana, 186
land routes, 156, 169, 198, 236, 245
   See also caravan routes
language and languages, 154, 155, 156, 181, 242, 247

Latin, 247
Lavoisier, A., 48
law and laws, 81, 96, 107, 137, 148, 187, 194, 245–246
Lebanon, 21, 153
Les Trois Frères (cave), 48
Lethe, 131
Libya, 147
Li Érh-Lang, 189
Lily-lake, 131
lingua franca, 154, 156
Li Ping, 189
Litani, 21
Little Khumdan glacier, 26, 27
Lloyd, Seton, *quoted* 134, 275
London, 23, 28, 139
Lo R., 189
Loyang, 249
Luxor, 70
Lydia, 105, 149
Lyons, 195

Maanjet, 126
Maas R., 96
Macedonia and Macedonians, 155, 158, 165
machines, 39, 80, 219, 221, 224, 225, 226, 227, 246, 264, 267
See also under name of machine
Madras, 72
Magdalenian culture, 40, 42–43, 44, 49, 81
magic, 36, 49, 50, 53, 71, 76, 78, 119, 120, 136, 137
Malabar, 159, 167
Malay, 159, 170
Malikshāh, 247
Mandrocles, 180
Mansur, 243
map making and maps, 205, 207, 213
Marco Polo, 250
Marcus Aurelius. *See* Antoninus, Marcus Aurelius
Marib dam, 83, 93, 237, 239
Mark Antony. *See* Antony, Mark
Marseilles, 82–83, 203
marshes, 59, 63, 188, 191, 237, 241, 267

Massilia, 170
Maurya empire, 160
Mecca, 104, 248
mechanics, 252, 264, 265, 267, 273
Medes, 142
Media, 147
medicine, 20, 38, 243, 247
Mediterranean, 21, 57, 72, 87, 132, 135, 137, 143, 151, 152, 158, 159, 161, 163, 193, 196
Megasthenes, 158–159, 185, 203
Mekong R., 209
Memphis, 87, 92, 97, 153, 242
Menaka, 123
Menes, 92
Mesket, 126
Mesopotamia and Mesopotamians, 55, 62, 63, 64, 65, 68, 70, 74, 83, 84, 90, 93, 97, 104, 108, 126, 127, 128, 131, 135, 136, 150, 154, 157, 158, 165, 185, 188, 201, 202, 273
metallurgy and metals, 81, 254, 255, 262
Metrodorus, 233
Middle East, 54, 57, 69, 74, 89, 103, 184, 243, 249
Middle West, 26
Miletus, 201
milling and mills, 224, 227, 252, 254
mill wheels. *See* water wheels
Min R., 199
Mississippi, 24, 25, 90
Mithridates, 164, 168, 191
Moab, 86, 103
Mohammed, 240
Mohenjo-Daro, 85, 87, 97, 261
Mongols, 250
Monongahela R., 25
monotheism, 154
monsoon, 185, 186
trade, 169, 172
Morocco, 253
Moses, 106, 133
Moslems, 240, 242
mosquitoes, 267
Mycenae, 86
mythology and myths, 131–133, 137, 201, 268–272

Nabataeans, 86, 197
Nabopolassar, 139, 142
Napoleon, 162
Naramsin, 130
Narbada R., 167, 170
Nearchus, 156, 157, 181
Nebuchadnezzar, 100, 111, 139, 142
Necho, 152, 161
Needham, Joseph, 7, *quoted* 190, *quoted* 208, *quoted* 251, 275
Nefertiti, 139
Negev, 197, 198
Nehru, Jawaharlal, *quoted* 31
neolithic man, 62, 77, 82
    See also New Stone Age
Nero, 168
Nerva, 194
Nessus, 132
New Mexico, 196
New Stone Age, 29
Nile, 24, 54, 56, 57, 59, 63, 74, 77, 78, 80, 82, 85, 86, 89, 90, 91, 94, 95, 98, 107, 122, 124, 125, 126, 131, 132, 138, 139, 144, 152, 153, 161, 162, 202, 209, 212, 214, 215, 216, 219, 237, 241, 245, 253, 257
Nilometer, 92, 241
Nîmes, 195
Nimrud, 93, 210
Nineveh, 69, 83, 87, 95, 97, 108, 109, 110, 112, 113, 142, 243
Nine Ways, 119
Ninurta, 127, 188
Nippur, 150
Nisibis, 175, 176
Noah, 128
norias, 229, 230, 231, 252
North Africa, 184, 193, 195, 212, 237, 245
North America, 25, 51
North Carolina, 25
Nubia, 46, 91

oases, 85, 184, 240, 241
Ob, 26
Oceanus R., 83, 132, 152
Ohio R., 24, 25
"Old Red Sandstone," 23

Old Stone Age, 29, 35
Oman, 184
Omar, *quoted* 248
Omayyads, 241, 242
Onesicrates, 181
Orontes R., 21, 93, 229
Osiris, 70, 125
Ostia, 170
overproduction, 232
Ovid, 263, *quoted* 269–270, *quoted* 272
Oxus (later Amu Darya), 132, 144, 148, 158, 160, 164, 167, 245

Pacific Ocean, 52
paddle chain pump, 254
paleolithic man, 34, 35, 37, 38, 39, 41, 48, 82
    See also Old Stone Age; primitive man
Palestine, 69, 124, 143, 158, 165, 196
Palmyra, 87, 239
Panama, 63
Pan Ch'ao, 168
papermaking, 251
papyrus, 84, 251
Parthenon, 148
Parthia and Parthians, 162, 164, 166, 168, 169, 170, 171, 207
Pasargadae, 147
pastoralism, 73
Pataliputra (later Patna), 238
Patna, 238
Patrocles, 203
peasants, 65, 73, 182, 190, 191, 267
    See also cultivating; farmers
Pennine Hills, 23
pepper, 159, 163, 167, 168, 173, 203
perfumes, 159
Persepolis, 147, 153, 154
Persia and Persians, 87, 100, 103, 108, 149, 151, 152, 170, 172, 183, 190, 235, 236, 238, 273
Persian Gulf, 24, 87, 88, 127, 132, 156, 157, 174
Pest (city), 104
Petra, 86, 165, 197, 239

284

Pharaohs, 94, 126, 130, 133, 143, 152, 161, 180, 239, 259
Phasis R., 161, 168
Phei Hsiu, *quoted* 208
Philo, 228, 252
Philonides, 181
Phoenicia and Phoenicians, 143, 179, 196, 239
pipe line, 104
Plato, 263
Pliny, *quoted* 166, *quoted* 167–168
Pont du Gard, 195
Pope, Alexander, *quoted* 202
population increase, 58
portages, 99, 152, 167
pot-hung wheel, 225, 227, 228, 230
potter's wheel and pottery, 69, 76, 84, 221
power. *See* water power
primitive man, 32–52
Ptah, 125
Ptolemies, 159, 161, 162, 163, 165, 169, 204, 241
public health, 246
public works, 189, 242, 247
pulleys, 221, 225, 228, 254
Punjab, 156
Punt, 112, 151
Puranas, quoted 123
Pyrenees, 40, 48, 54
Pyrrhus, 194
Pytheas, 203

qanats, 109, 110, 183, 184, 245
Queen Nefertiti, 139
Queen Semiramis, *quoted* 90
Queen Zubaida, 104, 248
quern, 220, 231
    See also saddle quern

Ra, 125, 126
rafts, 44, 46, 86, 95, 96, 98, 99, 113, 153, 175, 176, 244
rainfall and rains, 18, 57, 58, 59, 91, 185, 197, 198, 239
Reading Suggestions, 274–276
Red River, 170
Red Sea, 82, 94, 132, 151, 152, 160, 161, 166, 173, 216, 237, 241

religion, 81, 125, 131, 137, 154, 155, 181, 187, 194, 242, 251, 264
    See also under specific name
reservoirs, 100, 108, 185, 239
Rhoecus, 180
Rhone, 22, 170
rice, 150, 243
Right of Thirst, 240
River of Leprosy, 135
rivers
    control of, 217, 245, 246, 265, 268, 270, 271
    and death, 131
    diversion of, 30, 106, 124–128, 157, 175–176, 177, 182, 235, 265, 268, 270, 271
    divinity of, 118–119, 122
    healing powers of, 136–137, 200, 202, 215, 267
    pollution of, 134, 135, 257, 267
    punishment of, 117–118
    purification by, 124, 135–136
    sacrifices to, 119, 121, 191, 205
    sources of. *See* sources
road building and roads, 97, 151, 152, 236, 247, 262
Robins, F. W., *quoted* 195, 275
Romans and Rome, 70, 83, 100, 109, 162, 165, 167, 169, 170, 171, 175, 181, 182, 190, 193, 194, 196, 197, 209, 224, 231, 232, 233, 235, 237, 238, 240, 261, 267, 273
Roosevelt, Theodore, 246
rotary mills, 224, 227
Royal Road, 153, 157
Rudradaman, 186

saddle quern, 220, 222
Sahara, 98, 184
sails, 45, 98, 230
St. George's Day, 121
St. Lawrence R., 25
St. Louis (Mo.), 24
Salween R., 209
Samarkand, 245
Samos, 180
Santanu, 123
saqiyah, 230, 252

Sardanapalus, 95
Sargon, 99, 130, 133, 176, 241
Sargon II, 112
Sassanids, 171, 172, 175
Sattagydae, 147
Scamander, 119
Scandinavia, 23
science, 212, 214, 215, 217, 225, 227, 243, 251, 252, 260
Scipio Africanus, 193
Scorpion, 90
Scottish Highlands, 23
Scylax, 152, 156, 160, 161
Scythians, 142, 148
sea routes, 152, 154, 161, 170, 172, 201, 239, 241
Segovia, 83, 195
Seleucia and Seleucids, 158, 160, 162, 203, 243
Seljuk sultan, 247
Semiramis, *quoted* 90
Seneca, 211
Sennacherib, 102, 108, *quoted* 109–110, 111, *quoted* 112, 115, 116, 132, 142, 144, 180, 183, 236, 241, 245, 259
Seville, 243
shadufs, 68, 76, 83, 109, 113, 142, 220, 221, 224, 254, 255
Shakespeare, *quoted* 193–194
Shalmaneser III, 210
Shapur I, 235, 236, 242
Shapur II, 175, 176
ships, 82, 151
  See also boats
Shushtar, 235
Shyok, 26, 27
Sian, 249
Siberia, 20, 26
Sicily, 201
silk, 163, 165, 167, 169, 173, 203
Silk Roads, 168, 170, 238
silt, 215, 216, 217, 218, 237, 238, 267
Sinai desert, 104, 143
Sind, 150
Sinkiang, 164, 166, 168, 184
Sirius, 77
Siva, 122, 123

Skandagupta, 238
skyscrapers, 239
slave labor and slaves, 130, 181–182, 193, 194, 224, 227, 231, 232, 233, 252, 263, 264
sluice gates, 199, 235
Sogdi, 148
Solomon, 246
Solomon Islands, 72
sources of rivers, 202, 209, 210, 211, 212, 268
South America, 97
Spain and Spaniards, 104, 237, 242, 243, 248
Sparta, 75
Spercheios R., 118
spices, 152, 159, 167, 178
Stonehenge, 46
Strabo, *quoted* 203–204, 205, 212, *quoted* 214, 268, 275
Straits, 151
  See also Bosphorus; Dardanelles
Strymon R., 119
Styx, 131, 136
Subbaro, B., 7
Suez canal and Gulf, 152, 161, 241, 247
Sui dynasty, 249, 250
Sumeria, 64, 69, 71, 83, 89–90, 93, 94, 126, 128, 129, 133, 221
Susa, 87, 116, 144, 146, 148, 153, 154, 156
swamps, 59, 60–61, 65, 69, 74, 90, 97, 98
Switzerland, 34, 47
Syracuse, 133
Syr Darya R., 132
Syria, 21, 69, 83, 85, 93, 143, 157, 162, 165, 169, 173, 175, 229, 235, 239

tabus, 134, 135
Tanais R. (later Don), 202, 204
T'ang dynasty, 250, 251, 253
Tanjore, 266
tank irrigation, 185, 186
Tarim R., 164, 166, 170
Tashkent, 249
Taurus range, 99

Taxila, 156
Taylor, E. G. R., 7
Tearus R., 202
Teays R., 25, 26
Ten Thousand, The, 105
Thames R., 21, 96, 139
Thebes, 74, 87
Thermopylae, 101
Thessalonica, 231
Thirst, Right of, 240
Tiber, 82, 167, 170, 194
Tibet, 210
Tiglath-pileser I, *quoted* 111
Tigris, 24, 54, 57, 63, 74, 80, 82, 87,
    93, 98, 108, 109, 113, 126, 127,
    128, 131, 136, 138, 142, 144,
    153, 177, 210, 243, 247, 252
Til-Abni, 210
Titianus, Maes, 169
tolls, 168, 169
Tongking, 170, 190
toolmaking and tools, 29, 33, 37, 39,
    41, 42, 54, 63, 65, 70, 77, 219,
    262
Tower of Babel, 127, 154
trade and traders, 45, 46, 81, 96, 98,
    99, 106, 107, 132, 143, 149–
    151, 156, 159, 160, 161, 164,
    167, 200, 203, 236, 239, 242,
    247, 248, 249
    international, 148, 155, 159, 170
    routes, 83, 153–154, 156–157,
    160, 166, 226, 237
Traditions, 245
Trajan, 162, 170, 174, 194, 195
treadmill, 225, 226, 227, 254
tribute, 151, 165, 190–191
"Tribute of Yü, The," 205
trip hammers, 232, 254, 255
Trojans, 119
Tungabhadra R., 72
Tunis, 195
tunnels. *See qanats*
Tuscany, 203
Tu Shih, 255
turbines, 256
TVA system, 271
Twin Rivers, 64, 78, 127, 143, 183,
    239, 241, 243

See also Euphrates; Tigris
tympanum, 227
Tyre, 153
Tyrrhenia, 203

"upper paleolithic," 37
Ur, 87, 243, 261
"urban revolution," 80, 82
Usher, James, 78
Ut-napištim, 128

Valerian, 235
Vandals, 237
Vermuyden, Cornelius, 62
vertical water wheel, 255, 256
Vespasian, *quoted* 232
Virginia, 25
Vistula, 104
Vitruvius, 181, *quoted* 212–213,
    219, 226, 227, *quoted* 228–229,
    quoted 229–230, 231, 252, 253,
    256, 260
Volga, 104, 248

Wadi Gerrawi, 92, 94
Warring Kingdoms, 171
water conservancy, 30, 187, 242,
    257, 268
water control, 183–199
    See also dams; dikes; ditches, ir-
    rigation
water laws. *See* laws
water lifting, 66, 67, 68, 83, 220,
    221, 224, 225, 226, 227, 230,
    252, 254, 255
water mills, 30, 220, 224, 227, 231,
    232, 233, 252, 256, 267
water power, 219–234, 252, 253,
    259, 260, 261, 262, 264
water routes, 52, 93, 157, 158, 174,
    191, 198, 236, 250
    See also sea routes
water supply, 83, 89, 91, 93, 94, 95,
    102, 103, 106, 108–110, 182,
    193, 194, 200, 236, 239, 257
"Waterways Classic," 205
water wheels, 225, 227, 229, 230,
    256, 257

287

waterworks, 89, 107, 113, 150, 151, 182, 183, 193–198, 199, 236, 239, 240, 241, 242, 265
Watt, James, 48
Wei, 188, 189, 192, 251
wells, 74, 85, 87, 94, 104, 108, 109, 111, 181, 184, 220, 224, 227, 236, 248
Wen Ti, 249, 250
West River, 190, 209
West Virginia, 25
Wheeler, Mortimer, 168, 276
wheels, 221, 224, 225, 227, 229, 233, 234, 235–259
  water-lifting, 220, 230
"whole basin development," 218, 267, 268, 271
Wilderness of Zin, 197
windmills, 253
Woolley, Sir Leonard, 87
world community, 170–171, 172, 174, 180, 209, 213, 258, 259, 273
writing, 81, 84, 94, 130

Wu Ti, 163, 168, 191, 192, 207, 259

Xenophon, *quoted* 105, *quoted* 120–121
Xerxes, 103, 117, 118, *quoted* 119, 152, 177, 178, 179, 180

Yang Chien, 249
Yang Ti, 249, 250
Yangtze R., 124, 188, 190, 192, 207, 237, 249, 250, 258
Yazid Canal, 241
Yellow River, 24, 25, 188, 190, 191, 207, 210, 217, 237, 249, 257
Yemen, 239
Yenisei, 26
Yerebatan Sarayi, 198
Yezidi, 135
Yü, 188, 205

Zaghouan, 195
Zeus Leukaios, 136
Zoroaster, 155
Zubaida, 104